Ivor Gibson
May 1977

PELICAN BOOKS

A905

# THE ELECTRONIC REVOLUTION

S. Handel was born in London in 1913 and educated at Regent Street Polytechnic and University College, London. He has spent most of his working life in various branches of the electronics industry. He is a member of the Institution of Electrical Engineers and since 1956 has practised as an independent consultant. During this time he has contributed many articles on electronics and allied subjects to British and European technical journals. His *Dictionary of Electronics* is available as a Penguin Reference Book. Mr Handel wrote *The Electronic Revolution* 'because of a growing conviction that science and technology cannot be divorced from their social, economic and political consequences and that they must now become the concern of a much wider public than just scientists and technologists'.

S. HANDEL

# THE ELECTRONIC REVOLUTION

PENGUIN BOOKS

Penguin Books Ltd, Harmondsworth, Middlesex, England
Penguin Books Inc, 3300 Clipper Mill Road, Baltimore, Md 21211, U.S.A.
Penguin Books Australia Ltd, Ringwood, Victoria, Australia

—

First published 1967


—

Made and printed in Great Britain
by Cox & Wyman Ltd,
London, Reading and Fakenham
Set in Monotype Times

*Illustrations by C. Misstear*

# Contents

Research in applied science leads to reforms, research in pure science leads to revolutions.

J. J. Thomson

# Introduction

In the closing years of the nineteenth century an absent-minded professor of physics in Cambridge discovered the electron. He was Joseph John Thomson, born in Manchester, first a student and then a lecturer in mathematics at Trinity College, and in 1884 appointed Cavendish Professor of Physics when he was only twenty-eight years old. However little his thoughts may have been concerned with everyday matters (on one occasion his wife had to be reassured that he had not gone to the laboratory in his pyjamas) they were occupied to very good purpose in exploring the mysterious phenomena associated with the conduction of electricity through gases.

'I was led to investigations on this subject', he wrote, 'by having come to the conclusion that whenever a gas conducts electricity some of its molecules have been split up, and that it is the molecules which have been thus modified which impart electrical conductivity to the gas. . . . It was not until 1897 that I discovered that the decomposition of the molecules was of quite a different type from ordinary atomic dissociation; then I found that one of the bodies into which the molecules split up, the one carrying the negative charge, is something totally different from an atom and is indeed smaller in mass than one thousandth part of the smallest atom known.'

This characteristic statement illustrates the clarity and originality of Thomson's thinking and the extraordinary insight into the invisible world of atoms which enabled him to identify and measure the incredibly small electron, and to inspire his pupils and colleagues to discover the structure of the atom. It would be naïve to imagine that the discovery of the electron would have been long delayed if Thomson had been less brilliant. The time was ripe for it and in the main centres of physical research of the nineteenth-century world other scientists were hot on the trail. But this does not detract from the greatness of his achievement, which can be seen, in retrospect, as the very pinnacle of physical science in the nineteenth century and the source of its main stream in the twentieth. Thomson was a remarkable man who saw further than most of his contemporaries but not even he could have foreseen the profound effect his discovery was to have on the lives of the inhabitants of our planet in the twentieth century.

The theme of this book is that the discovery of the electron, and the investigations into its nature which followed, lead to a revolution in physical science. The application of the new knowledge in applied science, and above all in the applied science of electronics, led to a revolution in technology and is now bringing about a revolution in twentieth-century civilization which dominates our time and will determine our future. This may sound extravagant. After all, in the two-thirds of a century which has elapsed since the discovery of the electron there have been many other great scientific discoveries; dazzling achievements in technology have followed one another at breathtaking speed; violent social and political changes have been wrought in many parts of the world; monstrous weapons have been developed which threaten to annihilate us all. What is the significance of that invisible and infinitesimal bit of electricity – the electron – in all this? What do I mean by 'The Electronic Revolution'?

Before the discovery of the electron our knowledge of the nature of matter had advanced little beyond the conjectures of the Ancient Greeks. There was very strong evidence that all substances were made up of a limited variety of different kinds of 'ultimate' particles called atoms. The word 'atom' means 'uncuttable' and it was generally accepted that if it were possible to cut up a piece of, say, pure gold into smaller and smaller bits, the process would end with a large number of very small, identical, gold atoms which could be cut no further. A great deal was known about the properties of substances like gold, copper and iron, yet no one could account for the differences between gold, copper and iron atoms. The efforts of the alchemists, for example, to change iron, copper or tin into gold merely underlined their ignorance of atomic structure. Today we can break up atoms into smaller bits and change some kinds of atoms into other kinds because we know something of how atoms are made. Modern atomic theory began with Thomson's discoveries in the Cavendish Laboratory and caused a revolution in physics which in turn transformed the whole of science.

The searchlight which Thomson threw on the hidden world of the atom paved the way for many exciting new discoveries at the Cavendish and by physicists all over the world. The outstanding achievements at the Cavendish alone included: the discovery of the atomic nucleus and the proton by Rutherford, Thomson's young collaborator from New Zealand who was to outshine even the illustrious 'J.J.'; the discovery of the neutron by one of Rutherford's 'young men', James Chadwick; and the invention of the particle accelerator by two others, Cockcroft and Walton. Discoveries such as these inspired the great mathematical physicists of the early twentieth century who were then formulating their revolutionary theories. Planck's Quantum Theory, Einstein's Theory of Relativity, Bohr's model of the atom, the new wave mechanics of de Broglie and Schrödinger, and the uncertainty principle of Heisenberg and Dirac, were all concerned to account for the observed behaviour of electrons, protons and other fundamental particles of the universe.

The revolution in pure science rapidly bore fruit in many fields of applied science and technology, especially in the applied science of electronics. The vacuum techniques developed for the study of free electrons led directly to the radio valve, and the Crooke's Tube which aroused Thomson's interest in cathode rays was the father of the television receiver. The new electronics combined with the older techniques of the telegraph and telephone produced a revolution in communications on a world scale. If the discovery of the electron had led only to radio and television it would still represent a decisive factor in the shaping of our civilization – but it led to much more.

Electronics produced radar and guided missiles. It led to nucleonics and hence to atomic weapons and the exploitation of the immense store of energy locked in the atom. It gave birth to the electronic computer whose impact on society is just beginning to be felt. By the middle of the twentieth century a rapidly expanding, world-wide electronics industry was pouring out millions of parts for radio and television receivers and instruments for every branch of science and technology – instruments capable of unprecedented speed and sensitivity.

Electronic devices give immense extension to our senses. We can now examine structures too small to be visible in even the most powerful optical microscope and receive signals from radio stars which started their long journey through space ages before there was any life on our planet. Electronics combined with rocketry has enabled scientists to take close-up pictures of the moon and will make it possible for men to land on it. Electronics applied to medicine has already produced significant advances in diagnosis and treatment. Applied to biological research its first major triumphs in helping to unravel the structure of proteins holds out great promise of future advances in our knowledge of how living things are made and how our own brains function.

In industry, electronics plays the leading role in automation which is generating a second industrial revolution of wider social significance than the first.

In the home, electronically controlled appliances will replace domestic drudgery and in the office electronic data processing machines will replace mental drudgery.

The increased leisure which will result from the electronic revolution will create problems for society but it will also enrich and extend human culture and provide opportunity for the enjoyment of the vastly increased facilities for social and cultural interchanges which electronics will make possible.

Of course, all this is not an unmixed blessing. Like all other major revolutions the electronic revolution has its destructive and unpleasant possibilities. Drastic changes in methods of industrial production may result in hardship for many during the transition period. In the hands of selfish, greedy or foolish men electronics offers a powerful means of disturbing the peace and invading the privacy of the individual; of debasing and corrupting public standards in entertainment and the arts or of disseminating mischievous propaganda in the interests of private gain or political advantage. The leisure created by automation could become a destructive force in society. The new weapons of mass destruction – if they are ever used – will be guided to their targets by electronic means.

It cuts both ways. Electronics has also given birth to cybernetics which offers, for the first time in history, an effective science of government based on adequate information and communication. In the hands of a wise and benevolent government this could prove a decisive factor in solving the present problems of this troubled world and in fulfilling the needs and aspirations of mankind.

Whether for good or ill the electronic revolution is upon us and is gathering momentum. Since we cannot escape it we must try to understand and control it. This book will attempt a description of its salient features: its origins and development, its impact on our own time, and its possibilities for the future.

# PART ONE

# The Beginnings

# 1

# The Long Search

For far beneath the ken of senses lies
The nature of those ultimates of the world,
And so, since those themselves thou canst not see,
Their motion also must they veil from men.
Lucretius: *Of the Nature of Things* (58 B.C.)

IF an Ancient Greek, who had somehow been put into a state of suspended animation for twenty-five centuries, awoke in our own time he would no doubt find much of our present way of life very bewildering. Perhaps one of the things which would baffle him most would be the apparent importance of a fossil resin – amber – in the provision of light, heat, power and transport, and in countless mysterious devices which conjured sounds and images from thin air or tirelessly controlled the intricate machines of modern men. The Greek word for amber is *elektron* and though it was known from earliest times that this substance had the peculiar property of attracting light bodies to it if it was rubbed, the Greek philosophers never dreamed of the real significance of this property.

As long ago as 600 B.C. Thales of Miletus expressed the first crude ideas of the essential unity of nature and his belief in the existence of a single primordial element; but even he would have been astonished to learn that the particles which gave rubbed amber the power of attraction are of exactly the same kind as those which produce a flash of lightning. Democritus, who was described by Francis Bacon as 'a man of mightier metal than Plato or Aristotle', had established an atomic philosophy of nature by 400 B.C., and proposed as one of its principles that: 'the only existing things are the atoms and empty space; all else is mere opinion.' What would Democritus have made of the opinion of modern physicists that the atoms themselves are mostly empty space in which electrons move at great speeds around central nuclei?

The Roman poet Lucretius wrote eloquently of the ideas of the

Greek Atomists – of the infinite variety of atoms which they thought were the 'ultimate particles' of nature – but his words apply with even greater force to the much smaller and simpler electrons and protons which make up atoms. Whether or not electrons prove to be ultimate particles they are indeed so 'far beneath the ken of senses' that it is hardly surprising that their existence was not even suspected until 2,500 years after Thales. Yet although the Greeks had no theories whatever about electricity, their speculations started the long search for 'the nature of those ultimates of the world' which is the mainspring of physical science and which led eventually to the discovery of the electron. Had the Greeks been of a more practical turn of mind they might have invented the magnetic compass but in fact the magnetic needle was invented by the Chinese in the eleventh century and introduced to the West by Mediterranean sailors in the twelfth century, and it was probably this invention which stimulated the inquiries and experiments of William Gilbert of Colchester.

Gilbert, personal physician to Queen Elizabeth I and president of the Royal College of Physicians, was well schooled in Greek and Latin and it was he who invented the word 'electricity'. He was not only a shrewd and accurate observer but he was also a very practical man and in his famous book, *De Magnete*, published in 1600, he tells us simply and precisely how to make a pointer instrument for use in electrical experiments:

Now in order clearly to understand by experience how much attraction takes place, and what those substances may be that so attract other bodies, make yourself a rotating needle (electroscope – *versorium*) three or four fingers long, pretty light, and poised on a sharp point after the manner of a magnetic pointer. Bring near to one end of it a piece of amber or a gem, lightly rubbed, polished, and shining: at once the instrument revolves. Several objects are seen to attract not only natural objects, but things artificially prepared, or manufactured, or formed by mixture. Nor is this a rare property possessed by one object or two (as is commonly supposed) but evidently belongs to a multitude of objects, both simple and compound, e.g. sealing wax and other unctuous mixtures.

Gilbert's electroscope is the prototype of a long series of increasingly sensitive and accurate pointer instruments which have been indispensable to the development of physical science. He was able to show with it that substances can be divided into two sorts: those, such as glass and sulphur, which resembled amber in attracting the pivoted needle when they were rubbed; and those, like silver and copper, which did not. The first kind he called 'electrics', but we now call them dielectrics or insulators because they are able to obstruct the free flow of electricity. The second kind, which Gilbert called 'non-electrics' are our electrical conductors which allow electricity to flow freely. Because of this

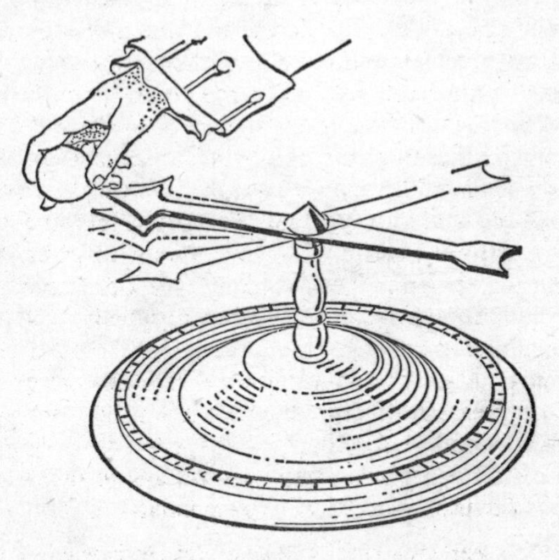

*Figure 1.* A seventeenth-century electroscope; simple instruments such as these were used by Gilbert to demonstrate the attractions and repulsions of electrically charged objects.

they are unable to store any electric charge produced by rubbing, as amber and other insulators can. Gilbert's work can be regarded as the beginning of experimental physics but he did not propound any *theory* of what electricity is. In spite of his extensive study of the lodestone and magnetic needle he did not guess at the fundamental link between magnetism and electricity but was inclined to treat them as quite distinct phenomena. He also missed the vital fact that there are apparently two kinds of electricity.

After Gilbert various amateurs, philosophers and scientists, including Otto von Guericke, the inventor of the air-pump, and

Isaac Newton, explored and exhibited the striking phenomena which accompanied the rubbing of various substances. At the beginning of the eighteenth century Hauksbee, Newton's assistant, showed that friction, besides generating electricity, could produce luminous effects in a vacuum and so (unknowingly) forecast fluorescent lighting. It became a matter of common knowledge that small light bodies, like feathers, could be made to jump about as they were alternately attracted and repelled by a ball of glass or sulphur which had been rubbed with silk.

In 1733 the French physicist Dufay noticed that sealing wax was electrified when rubbed with cat's fur but it then attracted an electrified body which was repelled by a glass rod. He therefore described two kinds of electricity: 'vitreous' – the kind produced by rubbing glass with silk; and 'resinous' – the kind produced by rubbing sealing wax with fur. In modern terms we say that in the first case electrons have been transferred from the glass to the silk and in the second case electrons have been transferred from the fur to the sealing wax, but Dufay gave no theoretical explanation of his findings.

The first electrical theory came from Benjamin Franklin, the revolutionary American who could also be described as the first international scientist since he was elected a Fellow of the Royal Society in 1756. Franklin recognized the two kinds of electrification noticed by Dufay and introduced the terms 'positive' and 'negative' to distinguish them. He decided to label any body which was repelled by a glass rod which had been rubbed with silk as positively electrified, and any body repelled by sealing wax rubbed with fur as negatively electrified. These arbitrary definitions remain today as the basis of our 'positive' and 'negative' and because Franklin chose to call negative the bodies which we now know have a surplus of electrons, the electron is now described as having a negative charge. Franklin guessed, without actually demonstrating the fact by measurement, that positive and negative charges always appear simultaneously in exactly equal amounts, and on the basis of this suggested that something which he called the 'electrical fire' is present in normal amount in neutral or unelectrified matter; that excess of the normal amount appeared as a positive charge, and less than the normal amount as a negative charge. If we interchange 'positive' and 'negative' and substitute 'electrons' for 'electric fire' in this theory we have essentially the modern theory.

Franklin combined theory and practice: he was the first to demonstrate the similarity between lightning and the mysterious something which was produced by rubbing amber or glass. He did this by his famous kite experiment in Philadelphia. In a letter to his friend Peter Collinson, F.R.S., dated 19 October 1752, Franklin supplies the practical details of his simple (but dangerous) experiment:

> Make a small cross of two light strips of cedar, the arms so long as to reach the four corners of a large thin silk handkerchief when extended; tie the corners of the handkerchief to the extremities of the cross, so you have the body of a kite; which being properly accommodated with a tail, loop, and string, will rise in the air like those made of paper; but this being of silk, is fitter to bear the wet and wind of a thunder-gust without tearing. To the top of the upright stick of the cross is to be fixed a very sharp-pointed wire, rising a foot or more above the wood. To the end of the twine next the hand, is to be tied a silk ribbon, and where the silk and twine join, a key may be fastened. This kite is to be raised when a thunder-gust appears to be coming on, and the person who holds the string must stand within a door or window or under some cover, so that the silk ribbon may not be wet; and care must be taken that the twine does not touch the frame of the door or window. As soon as any of the thunder-clouds come over the kite, the pointed wire will draw the electric fire from them, and the kite, with all the twine, will be electrified, and the loose filaments of the twine will stand out every way, and be attracted by an approaching finger. When the rain has wet the kite and twine, so that it can conduct the electric fire freely, you will find it stream out plentifully on the approach of your knuckle; and from the electric fire thus obtained, spirits may be kindled, and all the other electrical experiments can be performed, which are usually done by the help of a rubbed glass globe or tube, and thereby the sameness of the electrical matter with that of lightning completely demonstrated.

Franklin can also be credited with the first practical application of electricity, since he literally brought it down to earth with the invention of the lightning conductor in 1753. Though he had not the slightest experimental evidence that electricity was granular in nature he made a remarkably inspired guess when he said: 'The electrical matter consists of particles extremely subtle, since it can permeate common matter, even the densest, with such

*Figure 2.* Benjamin Franklin draws 'electric fire' from thunder clouds with a paper kite.

freedom and ease as not to receive any appreciable resistance.' So Franklin was the first to draw attention to the physical structure and properties of the mysterious 'electric fluid', though he could not have dreamed that one day individual particles of this fluid would be tracked down, isolated and measured.

Franklin's one-fluid theory of electricity seems to have been forgotten or ignored for more than a century and the two-fluid theory became fashionable among eighteenth-century physicists. This postulated the existence of two weightless fluids which acted as positive and negative electricity. Matter in the neutral state contained equal amounts of these fluids but became charged positively or negatively when one or the other was in excess. This theory could be applied consistently to explain the observed behaviour of electrified bodies but it was a step backward from Franklin's simpler theory and it had the effect of divorcing electricity from matter. As Thomson remarked in his Silliman lectures in 1903: 'the physicists and mathematicians who did most to develop the fluid theories . . . refined and idealized their conceptions of the fluids themselves until any reference to their physical properties was considered almost indelicate.'

Until methods were found of measuring them with reasonable accuracy, both electricity and magnetism were bound to remain mysterious invisible fluids. As often happens in science and technology it was the invention of a new instrument which led to further progress. This was the torsion balance, invented independently by Michell in England about 1770 and by Coulomb in France about ten years later. The basic principle of the torsion balance was the use of the magnetic needle suspended by a fine fibre, and with an instrument of this type the English chemist and physicist Henry Cavendish discovered the law of force between two charged bodies in 1771. Coulomb made a sensitive torsion balance which enabled him to perform much more accurate measurements than Cavendish and he published these in detail in 1785. They proved that, like the force of gravity, the action of the electric fluid, whether repulsive or attractive, was inversely as the square of the distance between the charged bodies.

Coulomb's work was recognized by naming the unit of electric charge after him. With his genius for precise measurement he would have been fascinated to learn that the charge on an

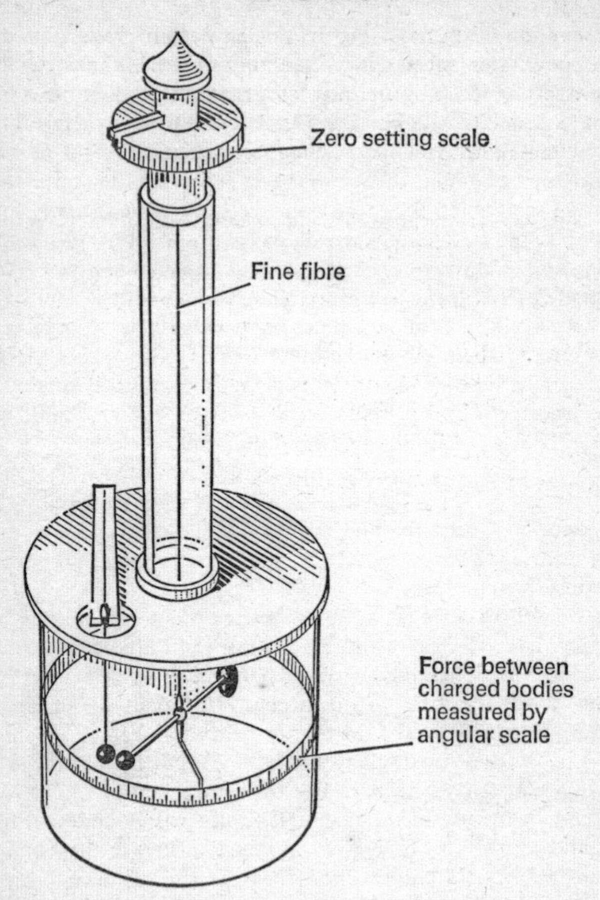


*Figure 3.* The torsion balance; it permitted accurate measurements of the forces between electrically charged bodies.

individual electron is so small that it would take nearly twenty million, million, million ($2 \times 10^{19}$) of such charges to make up one coulomb, which is roughly the amount of electricity passing through the filament of a 100-watt lamp in two seconds.

A major advance in the science of electricity was made possible by the invention of the first 'pile' or electric battery by an Italian professor of physics, Alessandro Volta, about 1800. He discovered that electricity could be generated by the moistened surfaces of two different metals in contact. Volta described his invention in a letter, dated 20 March 1800, to Sir Joseph Banks, President of the Royal Society:

> Yes! the apparatus of which I speak, and which will doubtless astonish you, is only an assemblage of a number of good conductors of different sorts arranged in a certain way. 30, 40, 60 pieces or more of copper, or better of silver, each in contact with a piece of tin, or what is much better, of zinc, and an equal number of layers of water or some other liquid which is a better conductor than pure water, such as salt-water or lye and so forth, or pieces of cardboard or of leather, etc., well soaked with these liquids; when such layers are interposed between each couple or combination of the two different metals, such an alternative series of these three sorts of conductors always in the same order, constitutes my new instrument.

*Figure 4.* Volta's battery, the first steady and reliable source of electric power.

Volta pointed out the great advantage of this source of electricity over other means available up to then, such as Leyden jars or friction devices, since it 'does not need, as they do, to be charged in advance by means of an outside source; and in that it can give the disturbance every time that it is properly touched, no matter how often'.

Volta's primitive battery provided the first steady and reliable source of electric power and with it he was able to improve the technique of measuring moving electricity (e.g. electric current moving along wire conductors) as distinct from static electricity on charged bodies. His great contributions to electricity and electrochemistry were officially recognized in 1893 when his name was given to the unit of electromotive force. But although the voltaic pile marked the beginning of a general advance in electrical technology, in the early part of the nineteenth century there was still no theory of the granular nature of electricity.

It was not until 1833 that the first experimental evidence was produced that the electric fluid was made up of particles. This was due to the experimental genius of Michael Faraday, who started life as a bookbinder's errand boy and was elected to the Royal Society by the time he was thirty-three. He showed that when a given quantity of electricity was passed through a solution of any chemical compound of hydrogen, the same amount of hydrogen gas appeared at the negative terminal. Moreover, the quantity of electricity which liberated one gram of hydrogen gas from solution also deposited exactly 107·05 grams of silver from a solution of a silver compound. Now since it was known that the weight of a silver atom is 107·05 times the weight of a hydrogen atom, this was pretty clear evidence that in solution the silver atom and the hydrogen atom are associated with the same amount of electricity. Faraday also discovered that all atoms which combine with one atom of hydrogen, called univalent atoms, carry an identical quantity of electricity and that atoms which combine with two hydrogen atoms carry exactly twice this amount.

Faraday did not conclude from his discoveries that electricity was made up of individual particles. Ironically, it was Faraday himself who started the new trend in the nineteenth century conception of electricity as something resulting from the stresses and strains in the medium surrounding the electrified body. Since he could not accept the idea of action at a distance he endowed the medium between separated bodies which experienced electric or magnetic attraction or repulsion with physical properties. These were analagous to the properties of an elastic material in which forces applied at one point are transmitted to other parts by a progressive deformation of the material. However, it could be demonstrated that electric and magnetic forces act through a vacuum so that it was considered necessary to invent a universal intangible 'ether' filling the whole of space, through which these forces could act. Like the lines and tubes of force which Faraday imagined surrounding his electrified or magnetized bodies, the ether was a convenient mathematical fiction which was used with great virtuosity by Clerk Maxwell to establish the laws of electromagnetism. But it directed attention away from the nature of electricity itself.

Almost half a century elapsed before the real implications of Faraday's brilliant discoveries were clearly stated. In 1881, Helmholtz, in his Faraday lectures at the Royal Institution said:

> Now the most startling result of Faraday's law is perhaps this, if we accept the hypothesis that the elementary substances are composed of atoms, we cannot avoid concluding that electricity also, positive as well as negative, is divided into definite elementary portions which behave like atoms of electricity.

This statement might seem to have anticipated Thomson's discovery but Helmholtz was not at all sure that his argument applied to metallic conductors and conduction through gases as well as through electrolytes. He was prepared to consider the atoms of compounds in solution (ions, as we now call them) as carrying one or more negative or positive charges but he did not apparently envisage the 'atoms' of electricity moving along a wire or through a solid metal. Many leading physicists of the time, including Lord Kelvin, did not accept the atomic view of electricity and the dominant view in the late nineteenth century was further removed from our modern view than was Franklin's one-fluid theory. Most scientists accepted the view that matter was composed of a limited number of different kinds of extremely small but none the less real indivisible atoms. No one suspected that these little atoms were made up of much smaller positive and negative particles of electricity.

The firm experimental evidence which was to establish beyond reasonable doubt the existence of the elusive electron and hence the granular nature of electricity came from investigations of the discharge of electricity through gases, culminating in Thomson's work at the Cavendish laboratory. Faraday, in 1838, had noticed the phosphorescent glow which accompanied the discharge of an electric current through a partial vacuum, but it was not until about 1860 that detailed work was done, especially by Geissler and Hittorf in Germany. In 1869, Hittorf showed that the current

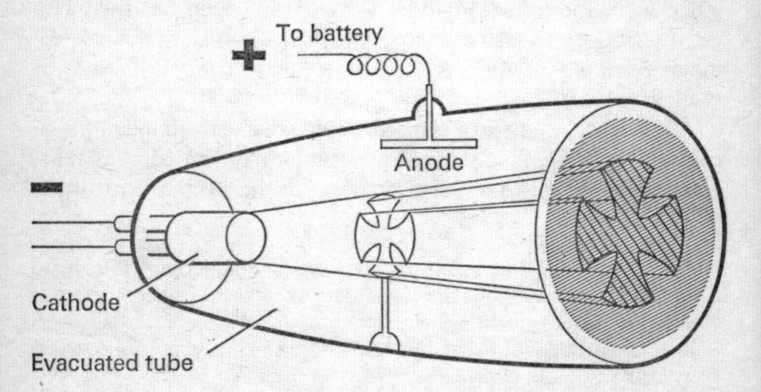


*Figure 5.* Electrons cast a shadow; a solid obstacle in the invisible beam of electrons from the cathode of the evacuated tube throws a shadow on the phosphorescent screen.

between two electrodes in an evacuated glass vessel flowed in straight lines which produced phosphorescence where they met the glass walls of the container. If a solid obstacle was placed in the path of lines which streamed from the negative electrode, or cathode, a 'shadow' was projected on the glowing wall. If a similar obstacle was placed in the path of the positive electrode, or anode, no shadow was formed. So the rays formed a one-way traffic: from cathode to anode and not in the opposite direction; they were therefore called 'cathode rays'. The German physicists thought that the cathode rays were waves: electromagnetic waves, like light waves, in fact, but of a different wavelength.

In England, Varley and Crookes found that when they placed the discharge tube between the poles of a powerful magnet, the cathode rays were bent out of their original path. Electromagnetic waves did not behave in that way and it began to look as though the cathode rays were made up of charged particles. In 1879 Crookes made an amazing forecast in describing his experiments: 'The phenomena in these exhausted tubes reveal to physical science a new world – a world where matter exists in a fourth state. . . . In studying this fourth state of matter we seem at length to have within our grasp and obedient to our control the little indivisible particles which with good warrant are supposed to constitute the physical basis of the universe.'

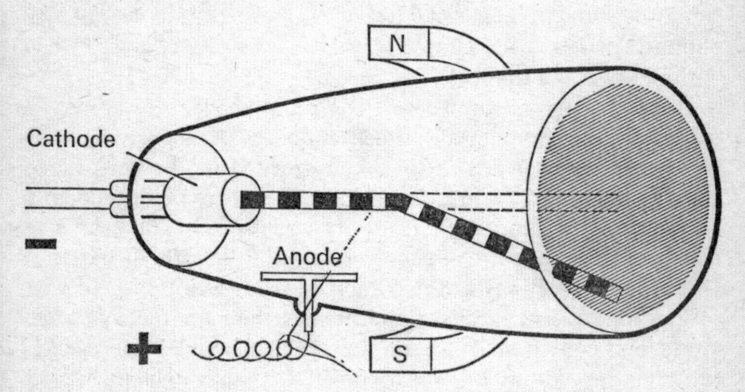


*Figure 6.* Cathode rays are bent by a magnet (see above).

By the last decade of the nineteenth century, scientists everywhere were taking a great interest in cathode rays, and the era of quantitative measurement of their properties began. The tools and techniques available for these studies had made great strides with the parallel advance of pure science and technology. Vacuum techniques had reached a considerable degree of sophistication and powerful electromagnetic fields could be produced by passing large currents through coils of conducting wire. Arthur Schuster, Professor of Physics at Manchester University, made some measurements on the rays in 1890. Assuming that they were charged particles he reasoned that their deflections in a magnetic field depended on three main factors: the greater their charge the greater the effect of the magnet and the greater their deflection; the greater their mass the more their inertia resisted the deflection; and the higher their speed the more they would be deflected. The measurement of greatest interest was the ratio of charge to mass as this could be compared with a well-known figure for an atomic particle: that of the hydrogen ion in electrolysis. Schuster's results gave a ratio for the cathode particles some 500 times greater than for the hydrogen ion. He could not imagine particles which were smaller than atoms and therefore proposed that the cathode rays consisted of intensively charged atoms. But the great German physicist Hertz demonstrated in 1892 that the extent to which cathode rays could penetrate thin metal foils ruled out the likelihood that they were particles as big as atoms. In 1895 Jean Perrin showed that a conductor becomes negatively charged when cathode rays fall upon it.

It was J. J. Thomson who, in 1897, first conceived the idea of subjecting the cathode rays to deflection simultaneously by magnetic and electric fields so that their speed could be determined directly (although the idea seems to have occurred independently to Weichert in Germany). Knowing their speed, Thomson was able to deduce the ratio of charge to mass of the cathode particles from their deflections in the combined fields and he found that this ratio was some 1,800 times greater than for the hydrogen atom. This convinced Thomson that the rays could not be electrically charged atoms but must consist of much lighter charged particles. In an article in the *Philosophical Magazine* in 1897, Thomson showed how his experiments resolved the controversy between the 'aetherial' and 'corpuscular' schools of thought which divided the world's leading physicists at the time: 'If, in the very intense electric field in the neighbourhood of the cathode, the molecules of a gas are dissociated and are split up, not into ordinary chemical atoms, but into these primordial atoms, which we shall for brevity call corpuscles; and if these corpuscles are charged with electricity and projected from the cathode by the electric field they would behave exactly like the cathode rays; . . . Thus on this view we have in the cathode rays matter in a new state: a state in which the subdivision of matter is carried very much further than in the ordinary gaseous state: a state in which all matter – that is, matter derived from different sources such as

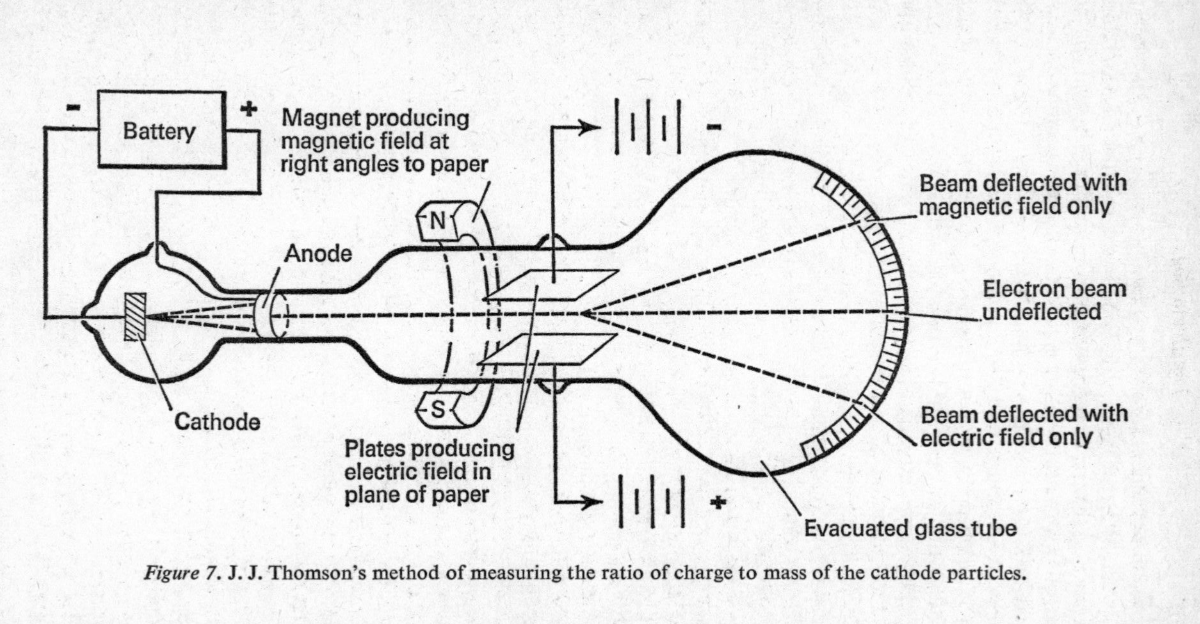


*Figure 7*. J. J. Thomson's method of measuring the ratio of charge to mass of the cathode particles.

hydrogen, oxygen, etc. – is of one and the same kind; this matter being the substance of which all the chemical elements are built up.'

Thomson reported his results to the Cavendish Physical Society, a newly-formed group which held fortnightly discussions on recent work, and stated: 'Cathode rays are particles of negative electricity.' It was here that he first used the word 'electron', a name which had been proposed by Johnston Stoney of Dublin in 1891 for units of electricity, to describe his particles.

2,500 years after it had been started by Thales, the long search for the 'ultimates of the world' had produced its first answer: 'the electron'.

## 2

# The Revolution in Science

THE discovery of the electron had the most profound effect on physical science. Scientists of the nineteenth century lived in a mechanical world firmly based on Newton's laws of motion, where an effect followed a cause as night follows day, and matter consisted of hard immutable particles like so many miniature billiard balls. Radiation had been brilliantly explained by Clerk Maxwell as a wave disturbance propagated, according to established mechanical laws, at a very great but finite speed through an elastic ether. When Hertz demonstrated in 1887 that radiation produced electrically was of the same nature as light, this was accepted as one more proof of the underlying mechanical structure of things, although to modern physicists it proves nothing of the sort.

This belief in a universal medium with definite mechanical properties which pervaded the whole universe was so strongly held that some scientists spent their lives trying to measure those properties. The famous Michelson-Morley experiment, first performed in 1887, was designed to measure the motion of the earth through the ether and when it showed that no such motion could be detected it caused some consternation among the orthodox. But it was the discovery of the electron and the subsequent application of the quantum theory to the interactions between electrons and radiation which finally shattered the mechanistic view of nature and ushered in a new scientific philosophy.

Many scientists were at first reluctant to accept the fact that Thomson had discovered a particle whose mass was much less than the mass of an atom of hydrogen, the lightest atom known. But the result was to be confirmed again and again in the world's leading physical laboratories with equipment of increasing accuracy and refinement. The invention of the condensation chamber in 1896 by C. T. R. Wilson, Professor of Natural Philosophy at Cambridge, marked a big advance in the measurement of charged particles. In this very elegant device charged particles are caused to attach themselves to drops of water which then fall as artificial rain to the floor of the chamber. The accumulated charges on all the drops are measured by an electroscope and the size of an average drop is calculated by its rate of fall against the resistance of the air. The total number of drops can then be calculated by

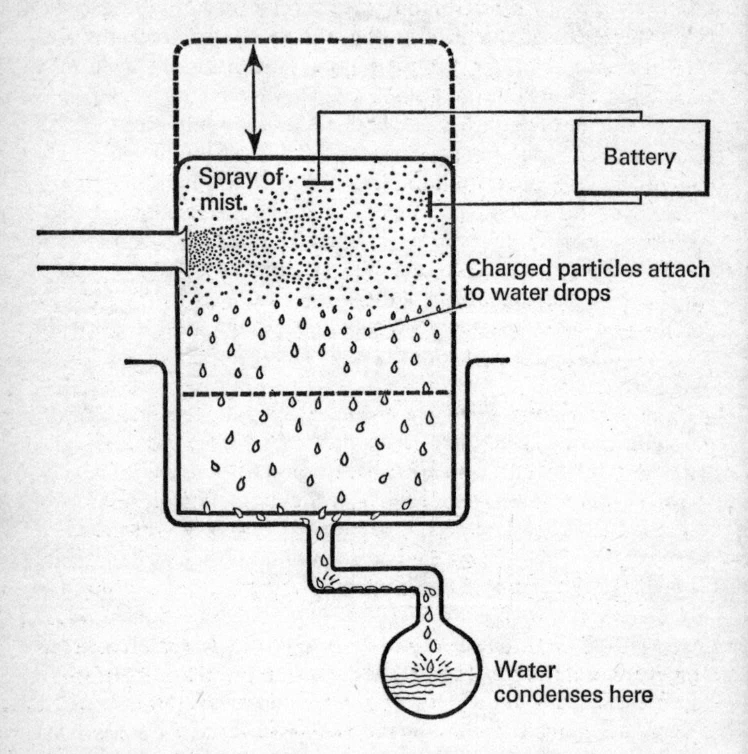


*Figure 8.* The principle of C. T. R. Wilson's cloud chamber in which very small electric charges can be measured by their effect on water drops.

weighing the total fall of water and all the data is available for estimating the charge on each drop. In 1899 Thomson used Wilson's cloud chamber to establish that the charge on the electron was the same as that on a hydrogen ion produced, for example, by the electrolysis of water. Since the measurement of the ratio of charge to mass of the electron was not in question the two measurements together gave a reliable value for the mass. Thomson found this to be about 1/1,800th of the mass of a hydrogen atom.

In the opening years of the twentieth century the American physicist R. A. Millikan conducted a series of beautiful and precise experiments to determine the charge on the electron. He

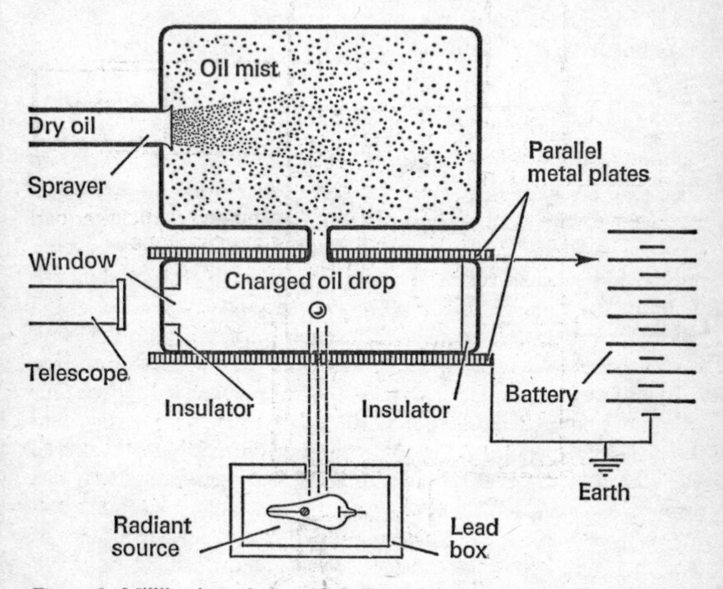


*Figure 9.* Millikan's technique for measuring the charge of an electron. The oil drop can be observed through the telescope and its movements in an electric field of known strength give the value of its electric charge.

imparted small electric charges to drops of oil floating in a mist of oil and subjected to a strong electric field. Careful observation of the speed with which the drops moved in the field showed that the charges on the drops never varied continuously but always in steps which were all whole multiples of the smallest change ever observed. This smallest value of charge was therefore accepted as the charge of a single electron. A large number of measurements established the value of the electronic charge with reasonable certainty. Some idea of the precision and sensitivity of Millikan's technique can be gained from the fact that he was able to weigh easily and accurately to one ten thousand millionth of a milligram (a milligram is about 1/30,000th of an ounce) whereas the limit obtainable with the very finest mechanical balance was about a millionth of a milligram. Millikan's results gave the value for the mass of an electron as 1/1,835th of the mass of a hydrogen atom. Measurements such as these convinced even the most sceptical that particles smaller than atoms existed.

## DISCOVERY OF X-RAYS

The interest aroused in the scientific world by the phenomena in electrical discharge tubes which led to the discovery of the electron also led to the discovery of X-rays. Several experimenters had noticed, to their annoyance, that photographic plates kept near electrical discharge tubes had been fogged. This aroused the curiosity of Professor Röntgen of Würzburg University and in 1895 he made a cathode-ray tube with a metal target in it to intercept the cathode rays. When the tube was switched on a screen covered with fluorescent material *outside* the tube began to glow. This could not have been due to the cathode rays which were known to be unable to penetrate the glass walls of the tube so there must have been some other radiation present. Röntgen found that this radiation penetrated a 1,000-page book, the flesh of his hand, and thin sheets of metal; but it was stopped completely by a piece of lead 1·5 millimetres thick. By 1895 cathode-ray tubes were well developed and efficient vacuum suction pumps were available, so that Röntgen was able to demonstrate that the higher the vacuum in the tube the more penetrating was the radiation, which he called 'X-rays'.

In 1912 the German physicists Laue, Friedrich and Knipping showed that X-rays consisted of electromagnetic waves of much shorter wavelength than light. X-rays were destined to have many applications in various branches of pure and applied science but immediately after their discovery their most interesting property was that of changing any gas through which they were passed into a conductor of electricity. They split up the atoms of the gas into positive ions and electrons which could then be studied under simple conditions.

## RADIOACTIVITY

A year after Röntgen discovered X-rays, radioactivity was discovered by Henri Becquerel in Paris. Becquerel, fired by Röntgen's discovery, put a box of photographic plates, intended for investigations of X-rays, into a drawer which also happened to contain a compound of uranium, and was amazed to find that the crystals produced an image on the plates even though they were wrapped in two sheets of thick black paper. This lucky accident led Becquerel to carry out a number of simple experiments which showed that the radiation from the uranium was not short-lived but left him baffled about the way in which it was produced.

Pierre and Marie Curie followed up Becquerel's discovery with two years of devoted and arduous work under the most adverse conditions, culminating in 1899 in the isolation of minute quantities of the radioactive elements subsequently called radium and polonium from tons of pitchblende ore. Radium was found to have more than a million times the activity of uranium.

While the Curies were tracking down and isolating the radioactive elements in Paris, the young New Zealander, Ernest Rutherford, had taken up the challenge to reveal the nature of radioactivity. By 1899 he had established that there were two kinds of ray in the emanations from uranium and labelled them alpha and beta. Beta rays, which were about one hundred times more penetrating than alpha rays, were examined by Geisel, Curie, Becquerel and others in 1899, using the technique employed by Thomson two years previously to measure the electron, and turned out to be high-speed electrons with speeds approaching that of light. In 1900 it was discovered that radium emitted a still more penetrating radiation than beta rays and this was called gamma radiation.

By 1903 Rutherford, working with Frederick Soddy at McGill University in Canada, had found that alpha rays were positively charged particles moving at high speeds, and in 1906 he showed that the mass of each particle was more than 7,000 times that of an electron, with a charge double that of the electron but positive instead of negative. Three years later he proved that the alpha rays consisted of the nuclei of helium atoms, that is helium atoms with their orbital electrons stripped away to leave the nucleus with a double positive charge.

The very penetrating gamma rays were not deflected by either electric or magnetic fields and proved very difficult to identify, but it was finally shown that they were electromagnetic waves of very short wavelength – shorter than X-rays and less than a hundred-thousandth of the wavelength of visible light. Rutherford played

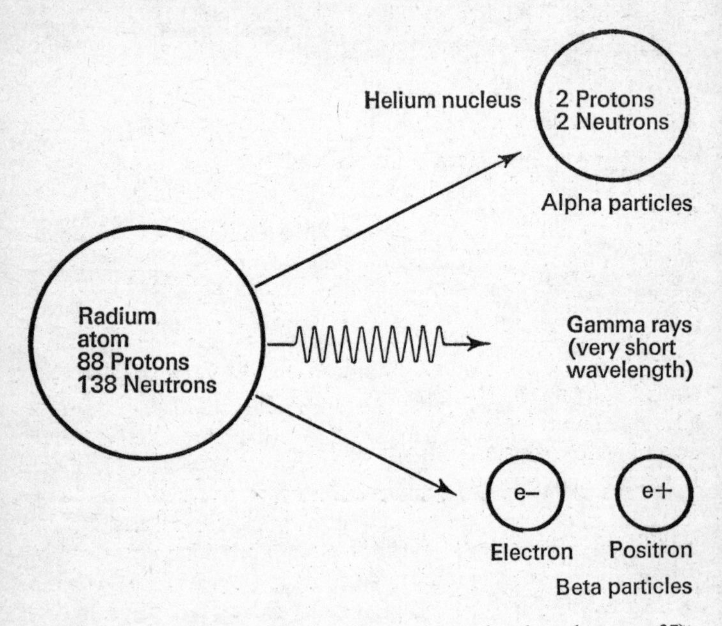


*Figure 10.* The way in which a radium atom can break up (see page 37).

the leading role not only in establishing the nature of the radio-active emanations but also in revealing the way in which radio-active atoms disintegrated spontaneously into lighter and more stable atoms with the ejection of alpha, beta and gamma rays.

Barely ten years after the discovery of the electron the indestructibility of elemental atoms was revealed as a myth and twentieth-century science was launched on its fateful journey into the restless inner world of the atom.

## THE QUANTUM THEORY

In the year 1900, while Thomson and Rutherford were beginning to take the measure of the atom, a paper was communicated by Max Planck, professor of theoretical physics in Berlin, to the German Physical Society which was to prove as revolutionary in mathematical physics as the discovery of the electron had been in experimental physics. In this paper Planck said: 'Radiant heat is not a continuous flow and indefinitely divisible. It must be defined as a discontinuous mass made up of units all of which are similar to one another.' This was a startling statement. At the time that it was made the idea that energy could be absorbed or emitted by a lump of matter only in definite steps and not smoothly seemed to violate both common sense and scientific knowledge, but Planck found that this theory was necessary to explain the way in which beams of radiation were emitted from a 'black body', such as the radiation from a hole in a metal ball heated to incandescence. The principle had not been suspected before because the steps or units of energy involved were extraordinarily small; in the everyday world they did not count but when dealing with emitters and absorbers the size of atoms they had to be taken into account. The value of each little step or 'quantum' turned out to be a universal constant of nature, like the charge on the electron. It applies not only to radiant heat, but also to the orbits of electrons in atoms, the photochemical effects of light, the wavelengths of the lines of the spectrum, the spacings of the atoms in a crystal, and so on. Planck's constant, h, was used by him in a sublimely simple formula:

quantum of energy = h times frequency

which shows that the energy required in any of the numerous kinds of periodic events in the world of vibrating atoms and molecules depends on the frequency of vibration.

Planck's theory was so revolutionary that its implications were not fully appreciated for some time (he was not awarded his Nobel prize until 1919) and it was none other than Albert Einstein who first drew the revolutionary conclusions. In 1905, when he was an unknown clerk in the Swiss patent office at Berne, Einstein applied Planck's ideas with devastating results to the photo-electric effect. This effect had first been studied by Lenard, a pupil of Hertz, who showed that radiation in the form of ultra-violet light could liberate electrons from the surface of a metal on which it impinged. The effect is produced in another way when ultra-violet light or X-rays pass through a gas and break up some of the atoms into positive ions and electrons so that the gas becomes an electrical conductor. Einstein's interpretation of the photo-electric effect was that not only did the energy of the incident light operate in separate packets or quanta, according to Planck's equation, but that light itself, and electromagnetic radiation in general, consisted of multitudes of individual pulses. Each pulse carried one quantum of energy and travelled with the speed of light. If high frequency radiation was pictured as a flight of bullets, low frequency radiation could be represented as small shot.

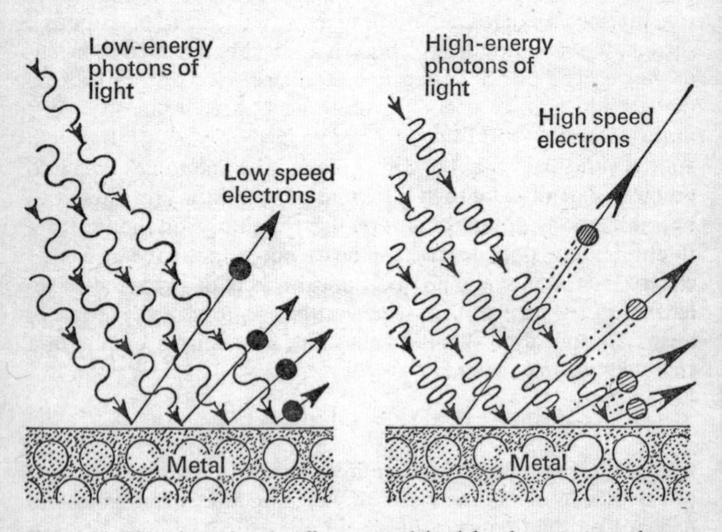


*Figure 11.* The photoelectric effect as explained by the quantum theory.

The theory that all electromagnetic radiation was made up of little packets – photons as they are now called – seemed to be a complete contradiction of the wave theory which had been firmly established by Maxwell, and a reversion to Newton's old corpuscular theory of light. Physicists were incredulous. But Einstein predicted that precise measurements of the photoelectric effect would show that if the intensity of light was increased the number of electrons ejected would increase but their ejection speeds would not increase; but if the frequency of the light were increased then the ejection speeds would be increased. This was a direct confrontation of the wave theory by the photon theory. The reasoning is that if the light consisted of photons, increase of frequency would result in increasing the energy of each photon and the extra energy would be passed on to the knocked-out electron and increase its speed. If light behaved as waves we would not expect the frequency to make any difference to the ejection speeds of the electrons. Subsequent experiments, especially those conducted by Millikan in 1915, confirmed Einstein's predictions. So the theory of the precocious patent clerk replaced the mature and tested theory of the great Clerk Maxwell, which had been one of the main props of physical science for half a century.

## RELATIVITY AND THE ELECTRON

Einstein was not too busy with the photoelectric effect to produce in 1905 the theory which we all associate with his name: the Special Theory of relativity. Like the quantum theory it was an attempt to account for the observed behaviour of matter and energy but it was concerned as much with the unbounded universe as the quantum theory was with the tiny internal world of the atom. However, the experimental evidence for the theory of relativity comes from the behaviour of electrons as well as from the behaviour of the stars.

The central principle of the theory of relativity is that all natural phenomena are the same for an observer moving at one speed as they are for another observer moving at another speed. Nature knows no such thing as absolute speed – only relative speed. The motion of any body can be measured only in relation to other bodies and the limiting speed of any body in the universe is the speed of light. Einstein showed that a necessary deduction from his theory was that the mass of a body depended on its motion and increased as its speed increased. The mass would increase rapidly as the speed approached that of light and would (hypothetically) become infinite if the speed were to attain the speed of light.

In 1881, almost twenty-five years before Einstein published his theory, J. J. Thomson had shown on theoretical grounds that the mass of an electrified particle would increase as its speed increased. Since this was in direct contradiction to Newton's laws, which assert that the mass of a body is independent of its motion, it was suggested that perhaps the total mass of the charged particle could be separated into a Newtonian mass which did not change and an electrical mass which did. After 1905 many physicists investigated the problem of how the mass of a moving electron varies with its speed and found that its 'total' mass varied in precisely the way which Thomson had predicted for the 'electrical' mass. The amazing but inescapable conclusion was that the mass of the electron was wholly electrical and depended on its speed.

The increase of mass of a body with its speed is very small until the speed is an appreciable fraction of the speed of light. Even a rocket travelling at a mile a second increases its mass by less than one ten-thousandth of its rest mass, but high speed electrons moving at three-quarters the speed of light will nearly double their rest mass.

### THE RUTHERFORD–BOHR MODEL OF THE ATOM

Rutherford, having established by 1911 that the alpha rays from radioactive materials consisted of positively charged particles comparable in size and mass with atoms, proceeded to use them with great effect to explore the interior of atoms. He showed that alpha particles projected through a long column of gas emerged mostly without any deflection from their course, but a few are deflected through large angles. This, said Rutherford, was about 'as incredible as if a gun fired a 15-inch shell at a piece of tissue paper and it came back to hit you'. By observing a large number of the tracks of his bombarding particles he deduced that the atoms of the gas consisted of a very small central nucleus, which was positively charged and contained most of the mass of the atom, surrounded by negatively charged electrons which together balanced the charge of the nucleus. Hence the 'solar system' picture of the atom, in which the 'sun' was a massive nucleus and the 'planets' revolving electrons.

The simplest atom, hydrogen, was pictured as a nucleus with a single positive charge having only one electron revolving around it. The most complex atom then known, uranium, had no less than 92 electrons to balance the nucleus.

The quantum theory again comes into the story. Einstein's application of the quantum theory to the photoelectric effect led to a revolution in the theories of the nature of light and radiant

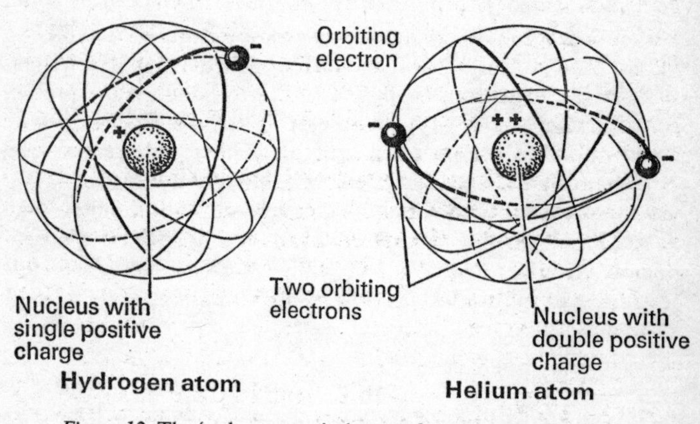


*Figure 12.* The 'solar system' picture of the two simplest atoms.

energy; its application by the Danish physicist Niels Bohr to the behaviour of electrons inside atoms led to a revolution in the theories of the structure of matter. In 1913 Bohr first put forward the idea that the motions of electrons inside atoms are subject to quantum laws rather than the classical laws which apply, for instance, to large bodies like the planets. This premise led Bohr to some surprising conclusions. Electrons were restricted to a finite number of fixed orbits and in each of these the momentum of the electron was fixed by the quantum laws. In ordinary experience it is known that any electric charge will radiate if it oscillates but in the atom the electron can perform its perpetual merry-go-round without radiating. According to Bohr radiation is emitted by an atom whenever an electron jumps or is transferred in any way from one permissible orbit to another. Thus visible light is the result of electrons in vast numbers of atoms jumping from one orbit to another. The lines of a spectrum – whether it be the spectrum of a candle or of a remote star – originate in this atomic hop scotch and the frequency of vibration of the emitted light is determined by the very simple relation:

> Frequency multiplied by Planck's constant = the difference between the energies of the atom in the corresponding quantum states

Bohr's theoretical predictions of the spectrum of a hydrogen atom, based on Rutherford's model for this atom of a nucleus consisting of a single proton with a single electron revolving round it, corresponded exactly with the observed spectrum. He was equally successful with helium, considering it to have a nucleus with a double positive charge and two orbital electrons. However, Bohr was unable to find the spectra for atoms more complex than helium, and this failure to account for the behaviour of extra-nuclear electrons in any but the simplest atoms led to the next revolutionary advance.

## WAVES, PARTICLES AND UNCERTAINTY

Bohr's magnificent attempt to explain matter as particles – electrons and protons – moving according to quantum laws in empty space was, in one sense, the last fling of the philosophy which had been founded by Democritus. After the First World War, which destroyed many illusions and cherished beliefs as well as human lives and treasure, scientists strove to recreate from the ruins of mechanistic philosophy a new natural philosophy which would be compatible with the sensational discoveries of the previous twenty years.

In the Europe of the 1920s a group of brilliant young mathematicians and physicists began to subject all previous theories of matter to a searching analysis. Their ideas were usually couched in the most austere mathematical language which was incomprehensible to laymen but even when these ideas were translated into ordinary language most people found them incredible. I think the reason for this was not so much that the mathematics were difficult (though they were difficult enough!) as that the ideas involved were so unfamiliar, that they defied explanation in familiar terms. Most of us imagine that we understand a term which we encounter or use frequently but this may not be true. We use words like 'wave' and 'particle' readily enough but we might be hard put to it to give a satisfactory definition of them. We know what is meant by 'wave' or 'particle' in the world we can see or touch, but what do these terms mean when applied to the interior of atoms or the behaviour of electrons? When talking about electrons as 'particles' we must not forget that the smallest particle in our everyday experience contains astronomical numbers of electrons, so that our mental picture of an electron as a 'particle' is not likely to provide a sound basis on which to interpret its behaviour. Consequently when we are told that electrons behave both as waves and particles we need not be worried because we are unable to visualize these strange hybrids: they do behave in this way, as we shall see.

In 1924 the young German physicist Werner Heisenberg, who had studied with Bohr in Copenhagen, took a completely fresh look at the atom. He rejected all word pictures of the atom, such as 'electron orbits', 'particles', 'waves', 'quanta of energy', etc., and concentrated on what could be actually observed and measured: namely, the frequencies and intensities of the spectral lines characteristic of any particular atom. At the age of twenty-three Heisenberg set out to produce a mathematical theory which would account for the spectral lines actually observed. Together with Professor Max Born of Berlin University he invented a new system of mathematical laws, known as 'Matrix Mechanics', which was able to make exact predictions of atomic spectra. In this system the electron 'particle' inside the atom appeared as an array of mathematical terms which certainly represented something more complex than a particle. The mathematics of Heisenberg and Born were found to have universal application in atomic physics and when applied to electrons in the free space around an atom or in the outer confines of an atom they became identical with Bohr's scheme.

Also in 1924, Louis de Broglie of Paris joined in the debate by putting forward the idea of a moving electron as a train of waves. With his system of wave mechanics he showed how the principles of quantum theory could be used to determine the frequencies and wavelengths of these waves. Two years later the Austrian physicist Erwin Schrödinger applied this idea to the behaviour of electrons inside the atom, replacing Bohr's orbiting electrons with the equivalent trains of waves, and showed that the permissible orbits were precisely those which contained a whole number of complete waves.

Experimental proof that the wave-like aspect of electrons was more than a mathematical fiction was soon provided. In 1927 Davisson and Germer in the Bell Laboratories in New York found that if they directed a stream of electrons against the surface of a crystal the reflected electrons were distributed in a diffraction pattern similar to the pattern produced by X-rays in these circumstances. And in the following year G. P. Thomson, son of J. J. Thomson, showed that the diffraction pattern obtained by shooting a narrow beam of electrons through a thin film of metal was similar to that produced by X-rays. In the words of de Broglie: 'We can no longer imagine the electron as being just a minute corpuscle of electricity: we must associate a wave with it.'

Heisenberg was not satisfied with the mathematical description of the dual nature of the electron; he was looking for the reality which underlay the mathematical abstractions. In 1927 he introduced the principle of uncertainty which states that in the nature of things it is impossible to specify the exact position and the exact velocity of an electron at the same instant: the uncertainty in the position could be decreased only by increasing the uncertainty in the speed, or vice versa, and the product of the two uncertainties was a simple multiple of Planck's constant. This extremely original principle, which at first seems to undermine the whole basis of the exact sciences, turns out to be not so paradoxical after all. We must avoid repeating the same old mistake, that of hoisting the laws of the man-sized world on to the world of individual atoms and electrons. Some very precise instruments have been invented to measure speeds and distances but however precise they are they cannot dispose of a smaller mass or charge than an electron or use a smaller amount of energy than a single quantum, so that, in order to affect the most delicate instrument conceivable in the slightest degree, at least one electron or photon has to be violently affected. Of course these arguments do not apply from the traditional or pre-quantum view: in theory at least a ray of light could be made as weak as desired and therefore could be made to have negligible effect on an electron. But, as we have seen, on the quantum view the energy of a photon is not reduced by decreasing the intensity, but only by decreasing the frequency; in fact we should have to *increase* the frequency of any radiation used to examine electrons until the wavelength became short enough to be comparable with electrons, so the nearer the radiation gets to 'showing' us the electron the more the energy of its photons and the more the electron is jolted.

Heisenberg's uncertainty principle does not affect the behaviour of the world in the gross but its transformation of the fine detail from an exact and predictable pattern into a blur of probabilities was a major revolution in scientific thought.

A synthesis of the mathematical ideas of Heisenberg, de Broglie, and Schrödinger was effected by the Cambridge mathematician P. A. M. Dirac, who published his epoch making book *Quantum Mechanics* in 1930. In this profound but abstract work, wave mechanics and matrix mechanics appear as special cases of a more generally applicable system. The philosophy underlying Dirac's work is that natural processes can never be described completely as happenings in space and time, and that observation of such processes is also one of the events which they undergo.

## THE SPINNING ELECTRON

The continued study of the fine structure of the lines in atomic spectra – especially by the Americans Millikan and Bowen – revealed the disposition of electrons in the atom. In 1926, two young Dutch physicists, Uhlenbeck and Goudsmit, introduced a new idea into the physical conception of the atom. They suggested that every electron within an atom is revolving not only in an orbit around the nucleus but also on its own axis. Whatever this idea corresponds to in reality it has proved very useful in practice in accounting for the fine details of atomic spectra.

Pauli applied the quantum theory to the spinning electrons and evolved a number of simple rules which enable us to assign electrons to any particular orbit and so construct a time-and-space model of the atom which accounts for all its properties which do not depend on the nucleus. The significance of Heisenberg's uncertainty principle applied to this model is that although we can never specify the *precise* position of an electron in an orbit, we can predict its *probable* position.

The conception of spinning electrons provides a possible explanation of magnetism. It is postulated that in the atoms of magnetic elements – such as iron, cobalt or nickel – the spins of electrons in certain orbits are not balanced as they are in non-magnetic atoms, and the resultant force of the unbalanced spins appears as magnetic force.

## COSMIC RAYS AND THE POSITIVE ELECTRON

300 years after Gilbert described the first prototype, electroscopes had attained a high degree of perfection and sensitivity. Rutherford used these instruments with great effect in determining the nature of the radiation from radioactive atoms. It was the electroscope which produced the first evidence of cosmic rays which were to change radically our ideas about the nature of the universe.

In 1910 the Swiss Gödel took an electroscope up in a balloon to about 14,000 ft and observed that its rate of discharge was somewhat higher than it was on the ground. This was unexpected because it had been supposed that unidentified but penetrating radiation which discharged electroscopes at the earth's surface was generated, like radioactive emanation, by the minerals in the earth's crust, and would therefore fall off in high altitudes. Little was done to follow this up until 1922, when Millikan, Bowen and others sent up into the stratosphere (50,000 ft) the first space probes in the shape of self-regulating electrocopes, barometers and thermometers in sounding balloons. The readings of the instruments after recovery indicated the presence of penetrating radiation originating either in the atmosphere or in outer space. To decide between the two, electroscopes were sunk in several snow-fed mountain lakes at different altitudes in California. The readings showed that the lower the instruments the less was the discharge, therefore the atmosphere above must absorb rather than generate the radiation. Consequently the rays must originate from outer space and further measurements showed that the radiation from above was at least eighteen times as penetrating as the most penetrating gamma rays then known, which would give them sufficient penetrating power to pierce the atmosphere several times over. These very energetic rays were called cosmic rays.

By 1933, measurements by Regener, Piccard and others in very high altitude balloon flights confirmed that the total cosmic ray energy hitting the earth is about one half of the total energy received in the form of radiant light and heat from the stars and that it was uniformly distributed over the celestial dome. Millikan and his co-workers calculated that the total energy in the universe existing in the form of cosmic rays was from 30 to 300 times greater than that existing in all other forms of radiant energy combined.

It is now (1965) generally believed that primary cosmic rays consist of protons produced by radio stars at remote distances from our galaxy. These are accelerated by magnetic fields inside our galaxy and arrive at our atmosphere with enormous energies. The high energy primary rays are nearly all transformed in our atmosphere into secondary rays consisting of all kinds of elemental particles travelling at great speeds, and it is these which affect our electroscopes on earth. There is little doubt that in cosmic rays we are witnessing the effects of the creation and annihilation of matter: a truly awe-inspiring process in which the relation between matter and energy is expressed by Einstein's famous equation $E = mc^2$, where E is the energy, m the mass, and c the velocity of light.

The new kinds of particles produced by cosmic rays were to trigger off yet another revolutionary phase in fundamental physics. Before the night of 2 August 1932 it was universally supposed that the ultimate building blocks of all matter were the two permanent elementary particles: electrons and protons. The proton had exactly the same amount of charge as the electron but it was positive instead of negative, and its mass was 1,835 times that of the electron. An elaborate picture of the motions and distributions of the extra-nuclear electrons in all the 92 known kinds of atoms offered a consistent explanation of their chemical and physical properties. But the structure of the nucleus remained a mystery. It was known that it contained most of the mass of the atom; that it occupied a mere fraction of the effective space inhabited by the atom's family of electrons; and it was assumed that it consisted of protons and electrons, the number of protons for any particular kind of atom exceeding the number of nuclear electrons by the number of extra-nuclear electrons.

But on the afternoon of 2 August 1932 Dr Carl Anderson, in the Norman Bridge Laboratory, U.S.A., took a cosmic-ray photograph showing the track of a single particle in a Wilson cloud chamber. After studying this all night he was forced to the conclusion that it was the track of a particle which had the same

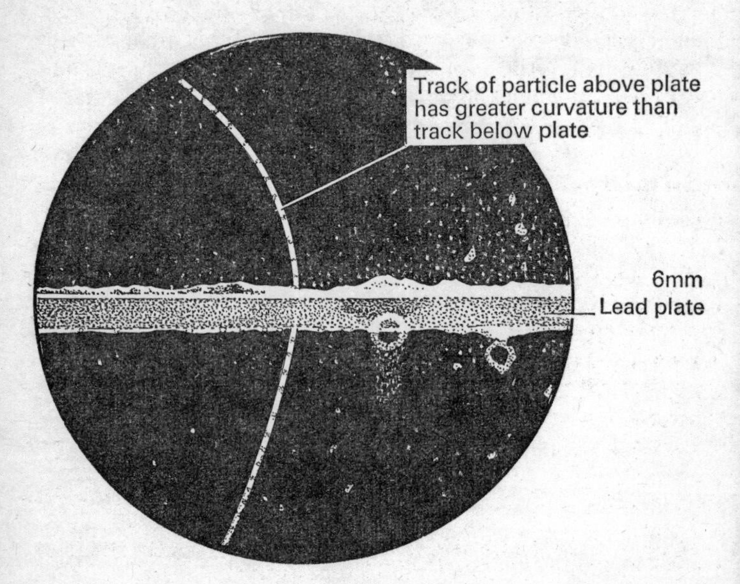


***Figure 13.*** **A copy of Dr Carl D. Anderson's photograph of the track of a 63-million-volt positron passing through a 6mm. lead plate and emerging as a 23-million-volt positron. This track could not have been made by any other particle then known.**

properties as a free negative electron – including the same mass – but with a *positive* charge and a very short life. Thus was the positron discovered and the proton ousted from its previous status as the fundamental unit of positive charge.

Subsequent work in America and Britain showed that the positive electron is produced by the impact of gamma rays as well as cosmic rays on the nuclei of atoms. Three years previously, Dirac, in his attempts to find a unified theory of matter, had found it necessary to include an 'anti-electron' with the same mass but of opposite charge of the electron. The positron exactly filled the requirements of the anti-electron and on Dirac's theory high

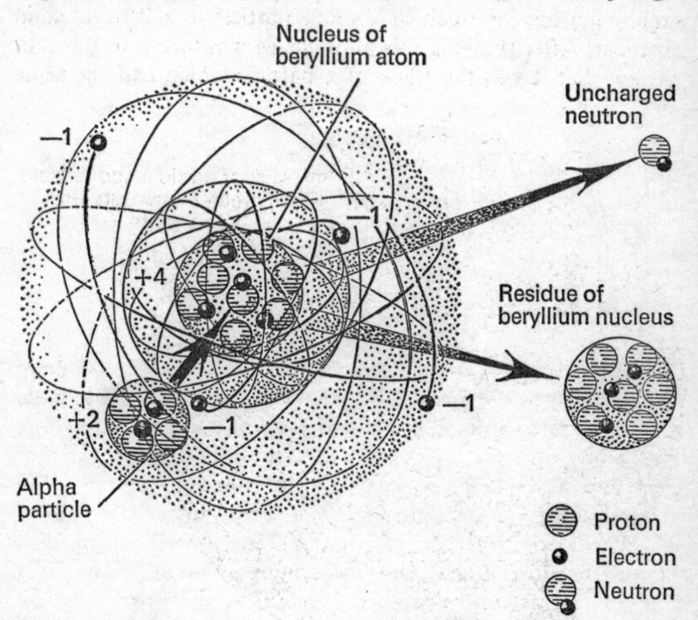


*Figure 14.* A neutron can be knocked out of a beryllium atom by hitting the nucleus with an alpha particle.

energy photons striking a nucleus may create an electron-positron pair; conversely, if an electron and positron are brought together they are annihilated, with liberation of energy according to Einstein's equation $E = mc^2$.

## THE NEUTRON

Another thrust into the heart of the atom was made by James Chadwick at the Cavendish Laboratory in 1932. He produced convincing evidence that when the atoms of certain elements such as beryllium and boron were bombarded by alpha particles from the radioactive element polonium, particles were knocked out of the nuclei which were of about the same mass as the proton but possessed *no charge*. These neutral particles cannot be identified in the usual way by their ionizing effects in cloud chambers or photographic emulsion since they cannot ionize, but because of their mass and penetration they can split up nuclei and their properties can be deduced from the charged particles which they knock out. Chadwick considered that the particles consisted of single protons and electrons in close combination, and he called them neutrons. Neutrons play an essential role in the nucleus and determine the fission and fusion processes in the smashing and transmutation of atoms which led to atomic weapons and atomic energy.

## THE RESTLESS ATOM

In the thirty years or so since the discovery of the positron and the neutron many more 'fundamental' particles have been discovered, but in contrast to the electron and proton, these all have short lives: some exist for less than a million-millionth of a second. There are now (1965) between 50 and 100 sub-nuclear states recognized but physicists can already discern an underlying pattern in the bewildering interplay of matter and energy which constitutes the nucleus. Just as the solid unchanging atoms of Democritus were transformed into a complex and mostly empty array of electrons round a small solid nucleus, so the nucleus itself has become a complex and turbulent system.

The electron still remains simple and indivisible and, whatever further surprises may be in store, the importance of the electron in the universe and its major role in the scientific revolution of the twentieth century has been abundantly established.

# 3

# The Growth of Electronics

> Faraday, Henry and Maxwell would have had little influence in the world without Bell, Edison and Marconi.
> J. G. Crowther: *Famous American Men of Science*

## THE EDISON EFFECT

IN 1879 that tireless and prolific inventor, Thomas Alva Edison, made the first practical carbon-filament electric lamp – a greater contribution to civilization than any that I know of by any of the princes, peers or politicians of his time. Lamps of this type, using power derived from the first electrical power network based on Edison's direct current dynamo, were a great success when they were first introduced but they had one big disadvantage: they were subject to blackening in use. While investigating this fault in 1883, Edison noted that, with certain conditions of vacuum and at certain voltages, there was a strange bluish glow in the lamp. He found that the glow was caused by an unexplained current between the two wires in the lamp which formed the leads to the filament. This current flowed in a direction opposite to the main current passing through the filament, that is to say from the cathode (negative) terminal to the anode (positive) terminal. The 'Edison effect' was never explained by its discoverer, but in characteristic fashion he took out a patent in 1886 for an 'electrical indicator' which was based on this effect.

As we have seen in the previous chapter, it was the intensive research by German and British scientists into the nature of cathode rays, and in particular the work of J. J. Thomson, which revealed finally that the Edison effect in an exhausted or gas-filled tube was due to the passage of electrons from the negative electrode to the positive. In the Edison lamp the electrons were produced from the incandescent filament, and the theory of the physical process involved – thermionic emission – was worked out in 1903 by O. W. Richardson, one of Thomson's pupils.

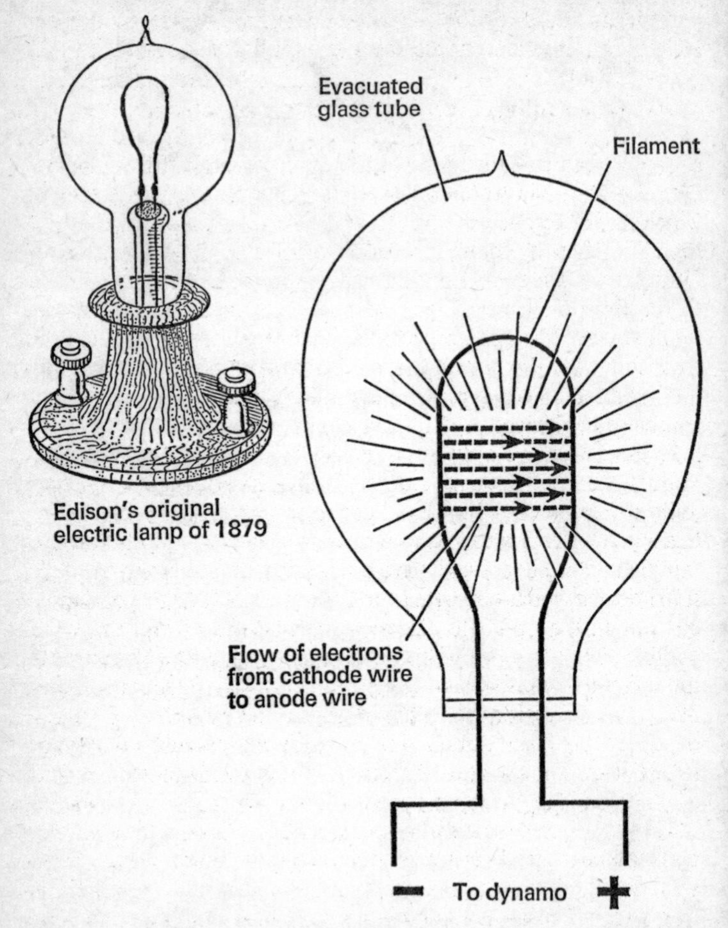


*Figure 15.* The Edison effect; investigation of the blue glow between the wires of the filament in the early Edison lamps led to the invention of the thermionic valve.

Richardson showed that electrons are emitted from hot metals by a process similar to evaporation.

These early inventions and discoveries led to the first two electronic devices which were to make radio and television possible, provide the basis for the electronics industry, and revolutionize technology – the thermionic valve and the cathode-ray tube.

## THE THERMIONIC VALVE

If anyone can be called 'the father of electronics' it is Ambrose Fleming, for he invented the thermionic valve, the first device in which free electrons were put to work. At the turn of the century Fleming, then a young professor of electrical engineering at University College in London, was appointed scientific adviser to the Edison Electric Light Company of London and became familiar with Edison's lamp experiments. He subsequently became a consultant to the British Marconi Company which was looking for a better detector of wireless signals than the clumsy and troublesome devices used by Marconi.

In the early days of wireless, at the beginning of the twentieth century, the signals used consisted of bursts of high frequency radio waves generated by starting and stopping a spark discharge in a sparking coil with a tapping key. At the receiving station the rapidly fluctuating waves had to be rectified, that is passed through some device which permitted the flow of current in one direction but not in the opposite direction, so that they would produce audible effects in a head-phone. The rectifying device then used – the coherer – consisted of a glass tube loosely filled with metal filings, whose resistance to the passage of current could be made dependent on the proximity of electrical discharges such as the wireless signals. The coherer was a finicky and inefficient device and Fleming had the idea of using the Edison effect as an alternative.

He put two metal plates in an exhausted tube: one, the cathode, was made electrically negative to the other, the anode. The cathode was heated to incandescence by a suitable battery so that electrons were emitted in a continuous stream towards the anode. When the tube was inserted in the aerial circuit of a wireless receiver, the anode became alternately positive and negative according to the fluctuations of the incoming high frequency oscillations, but electrons (being negatively charged) were attracted to the anode *only during the time it was positive* and were repelled during the part of the cycle when it was negative. The tube thus acted as a valve to wireless signals since it allowed current to flow only one way –

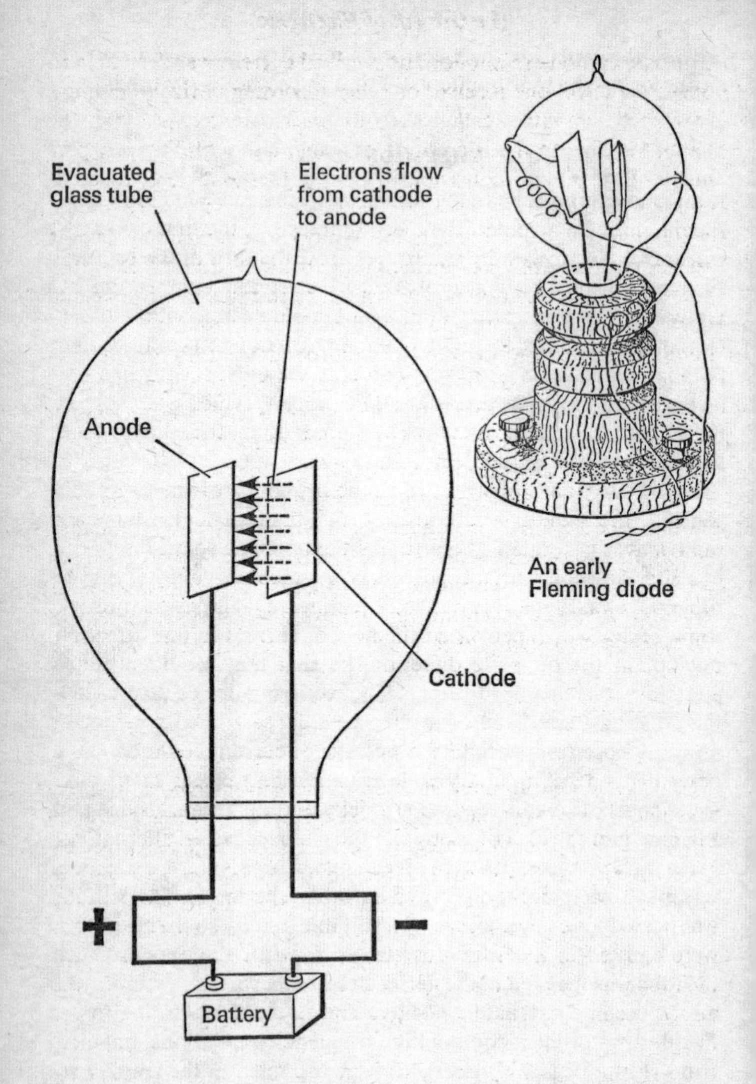


*Figure 16.* Fleming used the Edison effect in the first two-electrode tube to replace the coherer for wireless reception.

from the cathode to anode. The rectified current was then able to operate a telephone receiver or other recording device. Fleming's two-electrode valve, called a diode, was patented in 1904, the patent passing to the Marconi Company, although the only part played by Marconi consisted in having the good judgement to employ Fleming.

Fleming's valve proved to be typical of engineering devices based on an entirely new principle: it behaved under laboratory conditions but was not very satisfactory in practice. The crystal detector (the first semiconductor device), which was invented at about the same time, proved to be more reliable until the Fleming diode was improved by the Americans I. Langmuir and H. D. Arnold, who showed that it was necessary to have and maintain a very high vacuum in the tube. Although various inventors in different parts of the world lodged patents relating to the thermionic valve very soon after Fleming's first patent, thus setting into motion one of those prolonged legal wrangles over rival claims which were to become typical of the electronics industry, there can be little doubt that Fleming had the idea first. His crude diode was the forerunner of a vast family of increasingly complex and efficient thermionic valves and tubes which are now produced in hundreds of millions.

## THE TRIODE VALVE

The decisive development in thermionic valves came soon after Fleming's diode was patented. Lee de Forest, a young graduate who, in 1900, gave up a safe job as a telephone engineer with the Western Electric Company in Chicago to do experimental work in wireless telegraphy, was convinced that there was a great future in wireless. Like Fleming, he was looking for a better detector of wireless signals than the coherer and he carried out many experiments with gas-filled and partially exhausted tubes containing two electrodes. In the course of these experiments he introduced a third electrode, shaped like a gridiron, between the cathode and the anode. By connecting this grid to a separate battery he found he could control the flow of current between the hot cathode and the cold anode. He may have got the idea from the German physicist, Lenard, who had previously used the

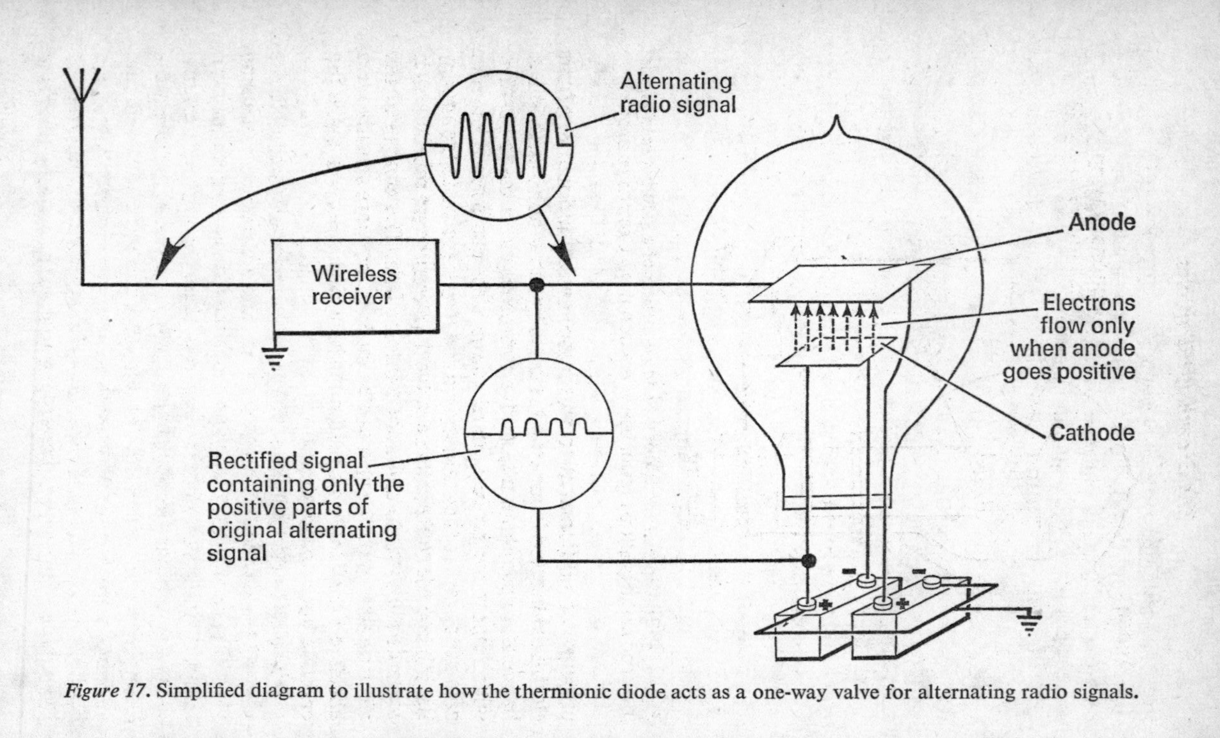


*Figure 17*. Simplified diagram to illustrate how the thermionic diode acts as a one-way valve for alternating radio signals.

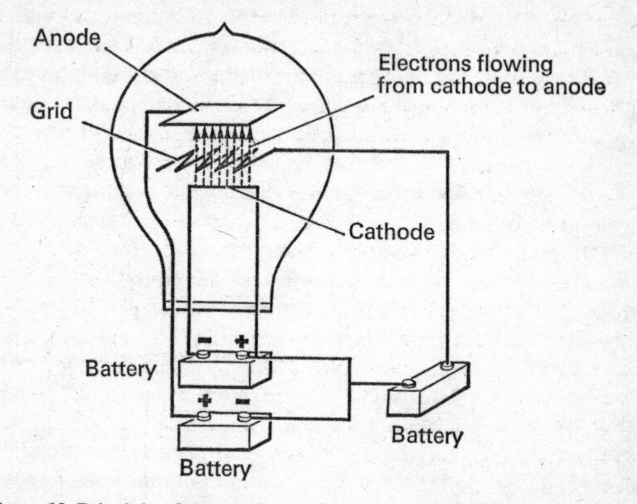


*Figure 18.* Principle of the triode; the introduction of a grid between anode and cathode allows much better control of the electron current.

principle of grid control to study the motion and nature of the electrons liberated from a zinc cathode by ultra-violet light. What happens, in simple terms, is that when the grid is made positive with respect to the cathode it draws electrons away from the cathode as fast as they are emitted and they travel on to the anode; but if it is made sufficiently negative the electrons are repelled back towards the cathode and anode current falls. The control of the electron stream by the grid can be made much more sensitive and effective than Fleming's method, which was simply to make the cathode hotter or colder.

When de Forest connected the aerial of a wireless receiver to the grid of his device he found that he had a detector. When the incoming signals went through a positive phase – which they did many thousands of times in a second – electrons were pulled away from the cathode and the anode current increased; during the negative phase some electrons were pushed back and anode current decreased. If a high voltage battery was connected to the anode, the voltage excursions of the anode in response to the fluctuations in the signal on the grid were much larger than the signal voltage variations. The triode valve not only rectified the alternating signals, in the manner of Fleming's diode, but *it also amplified them.*

It is probable that de Forest, who had a restless creative mind rather than an analytical one, did not fully understand the underlying principle of his audion – as he called the triode – nor did he grasp its importance. After he patented the device in 1907 he carried out very few experiments with it, and his attention was diverted to other aspects of wireless telephony. But in 1912 he experimented with audions connected in cascade, feeding the output of one tube into the input of the next, and found that he could obtain much greater amplification than was possible with a single tube. He thus created the first valve amplifier. The first application of electronics to telephony can also be attributed to de Forest since he used his cascades as telephone repeaters to increase the strength of weak telephone signals.

Not content with all this, de Forest continued his investigations with his triodes and discovered that they could be made to act as oscillators. In addition to their facility for rectifying and amplifying electromagnetic waves, they could also be used to generate them. This time de Forest appreciated the value of his discovery immediately and applied it to the generation of high frequency oscillations for wireless reception as an alternative to the unreliable arc or spark generators then in use. He designed a compact oscillating triode circuit, called the 'ultraudion', which was later used in quantity by the U.S. Navy.

The use of the thermionic valve as an oscillator for the generation of continuous waves was the main reason for the success of the heterodyne system of transmission and reception which remains the basis of radio and television transmission and reception today. Thermionic valve detectors and amplifiers are now being replaced by transistors and other semiconductor devices but there is still no really satisfactory alternative to the large powerful transmitting valves which are to be found in transmitting stations in every corner of the earth.

An interesting comment on the attitude of established interests in pre-1914 America to the invention of the triode was provided during a trial in May 1912 of de Forest and his associates in which they were charged with using the U.S. mails to defraud. (de Forest, like many another lone inventor, was constantly frustrated in his efforts to finance his inventions and he was an easy prey for unscrupulous financiers of the get-rich-quick variety.) The government prosecutor in the trial accused the defendants of selling stock in a company 'whose only assets were de Forest's patents chiefly directed to a strange device like an incandescent lamp which he called an audion and which device had proved worthless'. Thirty-three years later Dr I. I. Rabi, the American physicist and Nobel Prizewinner, described this 'worthless' device, in an article in the *Atlantic Monthly* for October 1945 entitled 'The physicist returns from the war', as: 'so outstanding in its consequences that it almost ranks with the greatest inventions of all time'.

## THERMIONIC TUBE TECHNOLOGY TO 1938

The Fleming diode and the de Forest triode were both at first unsatisfactory in practice because they were in advance of the engineering technique required to make them efficient. The necessary technique was acquired in the period 1910–25 mainly as a result of industrial research, first in the established telephone and lamp industries and then in the young radio industry.

In 1912 de Forest demonstrated his triode to engineers of the American Telephone and Telegraph Company who were considering it for transcontinental wire telephony. The demonstration was disappointing as the device distorted loud speech currents badly, and the average life of the tube was only about 50 hours. Dr H. D. Arnold, a young physicist on the staff of A. T. & T., deduced that the instability of the device was due to ionization of gas which had not been removed from the tube by the pumping equipment available to de Forest. The Gaede molecular pump, which had been invented in Germany in 1910, produced a much better vacuum than anything previously attainable and one was imported from Germany and used to produce a high vacuum tube. Arnold also substituted oxide-coated cathodes in place of the tantalum cathodes used by de Forest. By 1913 a filament with a laboratory life of 1,000 hours had been achieved, and by 1915 the A. T. & T. research team had improved the tubes sufficiently for them to be used as repeaters for the transcontinental line between New York and San Francisco.

Meanwhile, the General Electric Company of America was

also conducting research into vacuum tubes but from an entirely different standpoint: they were concerned with incandescent lamps and X-ray tubes. The team of scientists working on lamp research at G.E., which included W. D. Coolidge and Irving Langmuir, were among the few industrial scientists in the world to attain the status of the great European physicists. Irving Langmuir, quite independently of Arnold, showed that 'electron emission from heated metals was a true property of the metals themselves and was not, as has so often been thought, a secondary effect due to the presence of gas'. He therefore concluded that a 'hard' vacuum was required with the de Forest tube so that a pure electron discharge could take place. He invented a high vacuum furnace for this work, as well as a tungsten filament which had a long life and a good emission characteristic.

Between 1912 and 1925 numerous patents relating to the vacuum tube were taken out by A.T. & T. and G.E. (needless to say interferences between these were so numerous that many cross-licensing agreements on patents had to be arranged) and these two companies established a dominating position in the field, equalled only by the Marconi Company.

Little was done to produce improved vacuum tubes during the 1914–18 war. A very disappointing attempt at transatlantic radiotelephony was made in 1915 between Arlington U.S.A. and the Eiffel Tower in Paris. Even though a bank of no less than 500 tubes was used to transmit speech from Arlington, only a few faint words were recognized in Paris, and engineers from the Bell Laboratories were kept busy replacing burnt-out tubes.

With the establishment of the first regular radio broadcasting programmes in America in 1920, quantity production of 3-element radio tubes for the public commenced, and a similar process was repeated two years later in Britain with the establishment of the British Broadcasting Corporation. Older readers may remember the 'bright emitter' tubes which adorned the radio receivers of the twenties and made up in light and heat what they lacked in efficiency.

Improvements in tubes for receivers were accompanied by improvements in tubes for oscillators. The size, output power and efficiency of the latter increased steadily. The early maximum rating of a few watts was increased to 50 watts and then to 250 watts and by 1922 an experimental 100-kilowatt tube almost as big as a man had been made. On the receiving side, tubes which could deliver output power of several watts to loudspeakers had been developed by 1925.

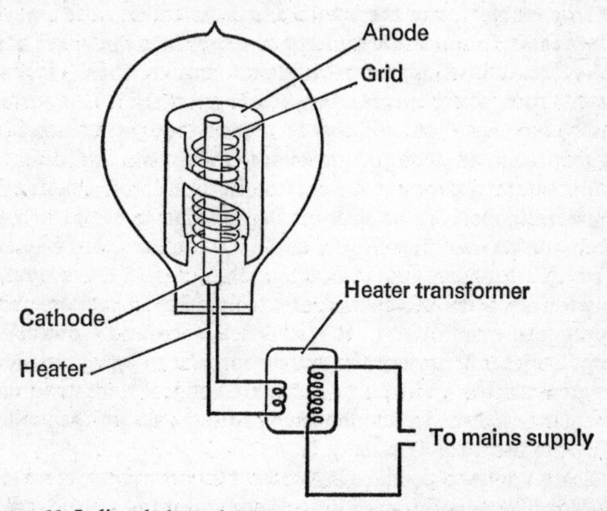


*Figure 19.* Indirectly heated valves; a heater wire inside the cathode allows the heater battery to be replaced by a mains transformer.

A big step forward was taken in 1927 with the introduction of A.C. tubes (or valves, as they were called in Britain) whose filaments could be heated by separate heater coils powered, via a transformer, from the main electricity supply. This meant that radio receivers could be designed to derive their power from a domestic electricity socket and the large and cumbersome batteries previously required to heat the filaments, which had to be recharged periodically, could be dispensed with.

By the 1930s the number of different types of tubes and valves was increasing rapidly and so were the numbers of each type which were manufactured. Greatly improved techniques for the production of high-vacuum tubes had been developed. Harmful gases occluded in the walls of the envelope, or the surfaces of the metal electrodes, were almost completely removed by 'baking' the glass envelope and 'vacuum furnacing' the metal electrodes before final assembly. A 'getter', i.e. a volatile substance which had a strong affinity for gases, was included in the tube assembly and used to absorb any traces of gas remaining after the tube had been sealed off. Oxide-coated dull emitters with a very high emission efficiency made it possible to produce smaller and better tubes with a long life.

Ten years of radio and radio-telephony resulted in the evolution of new types of valves with multi-electrode structures. The basic elements of all these can be classified broadly as: (1) an electron 'gun' to produce a copious flow of free electrons; (2) a positively charged anode or plate to receive the electron stream; and (3) a system of electrodes or meshes between (1) and (2) which exercised a control function on the electron stream. The gun might consist simply of a heated filament or, as with some cathode-ray tubes, an elaborate assembly of emitters and electron accelerating devices. The triode had the simplest control electrode assembly, consisting of a single control grid. The screen-grid valve (1928) introduced another grid between the control grid and the anode to reduce coupling between the input and the output circuits of the valve and so maintain efficient and stable amplification up to high frequencies. The pentode (1929) had a 5-electrode structure: cathode, three grids and anode. The extra grid, compared to the screen-grid tetrode, was called the 'suppressor' grid and its function was to prevent the secondary electrons which were emitted from the anode, when it was operated at a high voltage, from interfering with the operation of the valve. Beam power tubes (1930) introduced additional electrodes between screen grid and anode, but not directly in the electron stream, whose function was to direct and focus the electron beam towards the anode.

Converter, or mixer, tubes arrived about 1933. These contain two sets of electrodes in one envelope which share the electron stream from a common cathode. One set of electrodes is designed to amplify incoming radio frequency signals, and the other set produces its own oscillations which 'beat' with the incoming signals. The result is a converted signal containing all the information in the original but having a lower frequency and therefore being much more convenient to deal with.

In the early tubes the presence of gas in the tube was a nuisance but by 1920 'soft' tubes, in which a selected gas (such as mercury vapour or one of the inert gases neon, argon, helium, etc.) had been deliberately introduced, were found to have some very desirable properties. In hot-cathode gas-filled tubes electrons emitted from the cathode collide with the molecules of gas to produce positive and negative gaseous ions, and this action can be made to build up in the tube rather like an avalanche, so that beyond a certain critical point a rapid and massive discharge occurs through the tube. Large tubes in which the gas is mercury vapour from mercury-pool cathodes have been in use since about 1920 for the rectification of heavy alternating current to give a convenient supply of direct current. Gas-discharge diodes can be designed to give an output voltage which is almost independent of the current through the tube over a considerable range of current, thus acting as voltage stabilizers. In gas-filled triodes and tetrodes (called thyratrons) the control grid can be used to trigger off a sudden discharge in the tube so that the device acts as an electronic switch.

All these, and many other, advances in technique were embodied in tubes and circuits of increasing efficiency, speed of operation, range, amplification, output power and reliability. They were used for radio broadcasting transmission and reception, radio-telephony, early television receivers, sound film and gramophone recording and reproduction, and an increasing number of electronic instruments for measurement and control which were beginning to find applications in industry as well as in the laboratories.

## THE CATHODE-RAY TUBE

The cathode-ray tube, which is a member of the thermionic tube family, has played such an important part in the history, growth and expansion of electronics that it deserves a special section in this chapter.

The early experiments (1879) of Sir William Crookes with electrical discharges in exhausted tubes led to the discovery of cathode-rays and to his inspired guess about their nature (see page 29). The work of Hittorf, Elster and Geitel in Germany and of J. J. Thomson in Cambridge which revealed that cathode rays were streams of electrons depended on increased knowledge about the discharge tubes which they used and on the continued improvements in making and operating them.

In the same year (1897) in which Thomson announced his discovery of the electron, Karl Ferdinand Braun of the University of Strasbourg made the first cathode-ray oscilloscope and so initiated a major advance in the design and application of the cathode-ray tube. Braun knew that the electron stream between cathode and anode in the tube could be deflected by a magnetic field and he placed two sets of electro-magnets around the neck of the tube through which the electron stream was projected towards the anode. One set of electro-magnets deflected the electron beam from side to side, and the other deflected it up and down. A group of chemical compounds called phosphors have the property of glowing under the impact of electrons and Braun used one of these to coat a fluorescent screen which he placed inside the tube so that it received the beam after deflection. The path of the electron beam could then be observed as a glowing line on the screen.

Braun's invention led to intensive development of the cathode-ray tube which transformed it from a piece of laboratory equipment for the study of electrons into one of the most revolutionary devices of this century. The inertia of the electron beam is negligible and it will respond almost instantly to any change in the field through which it passes. The field can be magnetic, as it was in the original Braun tube; or electrostatic, produced by pairs of charged metal plates placed either parallel to or at right angles to the electron beam. Changes in the field influencing the beam are therefore immediately and faithfully portrayed on the fluorescent screen. Since it is possible to convert almost any physical phenomenon into voltage or current changes, these in turn can be used to vary the deflecting fields of the cathode-ray tube which then provides an elegant and sensitive method of observing and measuring rapidly moving or changing events. Events lasting only a millionth of a second can be followed easily on a modern cathode-ray tube, and with the most modern technique it is possible to observe and record an event lasting only one thousand-millionth of a second! This extraordinary sensitivity and speed of response of the cathode-ray tube accounts for its best-known application: the modern television picture tube whose manufacture is now a major industry in itself. It would be difficult to find another household article which contained so much of the most advanced scientific research and industrial 'know-how'.

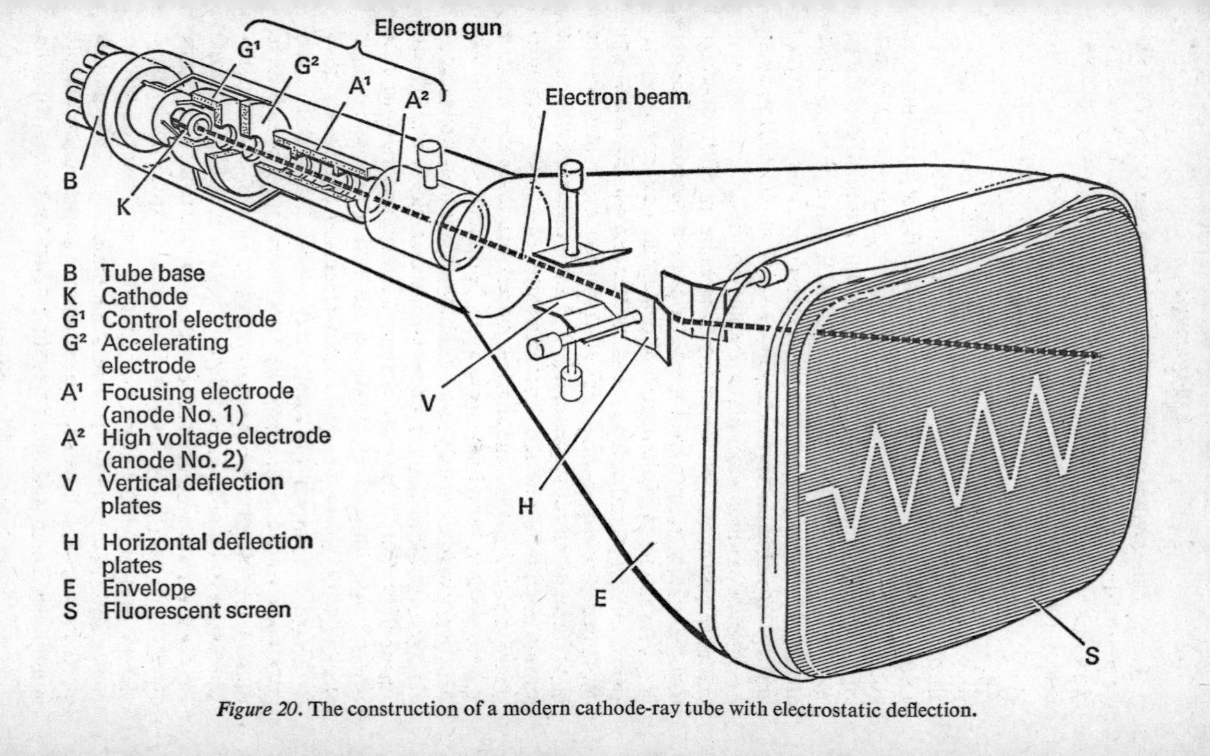


*Figure 20*. The construction of a modern cathode-ray tube with electrostatic deflection.

As we shall see in the following chapters, the cathode-ray tube was essential to the development of television and radar, and it has provided scientists and engineers with an invaluable new tool. It was a major factor in the growth of electronics.

### THE PHOTOCELL, THE ICONOSCOPE AND THE IMAGE DISSECTOR

The photoelectric effect – the ejection of electrons from atoms by photons of light – was discussed in Chapter 2, but the effect was known before Planck and Einstein provided the theoretical background for it. It was Hertz who discovered (in 1887) that electrons are emitted from negatively charged alkali metals – such as sodium and potassium – under the action of light. A photoelectric cell based on this discovery was developed in 1905 by Elster and Geitel in Germany, but these early photocells were low in sensitivity and erratic in performance and they remained mainly laboratory devices until about 1920. Industrial research into television and the introduction of sound films in the 1920s led to the very big improvements in photoelectric devices which made them, like the cathode-ray tube, articles in everyday use as well as extremely efficient scientific instruments.

When Dr Vladimir Zworykin, who had worked for the Russian Wireless Telegraph and Telephone Company, emigrated to America after the Russian Revolution, he had already conceived a way of transmitting and receiving images electronically. He joined the research team at Westinghouse laboratories and first worked on photocells. He produced a cell with a photo-sensitive element made of caesium–magnesium which was far more sensitive than any of the early photocells and was even superior to the caesium–silver cell which had been developed at about the same time by the General Electric Company in England. The immediate application of Zworykin's work was for sound films, as the 'Talkies' were a huge success when they were launched in America about 1926, and there was an immediate demand for improved photocells and amplifiers for the reproduction of film sound-tracks.

But Zworykin was looking primarily for a sensitive photoelectric device which would convert images into electric currents suitable for transmission in a system of television. In 1928 he

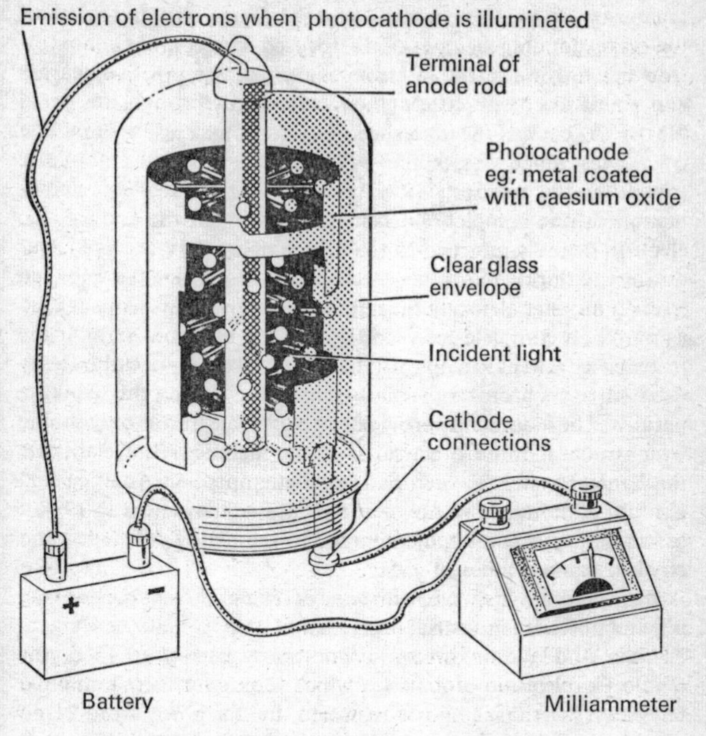


*Figure 21.* Principle of the vacuum photocell.

finally hit on such a device – the iconoscope. The iconoscope (the first camera tube) is a thermionic tube in which the illuminated image to be transmitted is focused by an optical lens on to a target plate. The plate is a sheet of mica which has been coated on one side with a mosaic of tiny globules of silver, each insulated from its neighbours. On the reverse side of the mica a thin conducting film of metal is applied and from this a connexion is taken to the input of an amplifier. An electron gun in the neck of the iconoscope tube shoots a beam of electrons at the mosaic and the beam is deflected so as to scan the whole surface of the target, the mosaic being traversed from top to bottom, line by line. Each individual photocell globule becomes positively charged to a greater or lesser extent according to the degree of illumination of the corresponding element of the focused image, and as the electron beam flys past the electrons neutralize the positive charges and small discharge currents are conducted through the metal film on the back of the mica sheet. This rapid succession of minute discharges which passes along the signal wire to the amplifier constitutes the television 'video' current (*video*=I see). After completion of one complete horizontal line scan of the surface, the electron beam is returned to the beginning of the next line lower down, and during this return sweep a 'blanking' signal is supplied to erase any signal during the return. When the iconoscope is used as part of a complete television system the electron beam at the transmitter is kept in step with that at the receiver – a cathode-ray tube – by synchronizing signals transmitted during the blanking periods. The iconoscope provided an electronic means of scanning which was far more practical than the ingenious but elaborate mechanical systems which had been attempted in America and Britain. Although it was a great technical achievement in 1928 it seems almost crude when compared to the highly developed and efficient camera tubes of today.

Zworykin did his work with the backing and resources of very big and powerful industrial organizations: up to 1930 the General Electric and Westinghouse corporations, and after 1930, the Radio Corporation of America which took over their radio and television interests. Philo Farnsworth, the farm boy from Idaho whose interest in television was aroused by reading popular electrical and radio magazines, invented and developed almost single-handed a system of electronic television which rivalled Zworykin's system. This was based on Farnsworth's very ingenious image dissector. Instead of scanning the image point by point and line by line, it dissects the image into a number of segments – equal to the number of picture elements required for the transmitted picture – by moving the whole electron image past a scanning aperture. The highly evacuated camera tube of the image dissector has a photo-cathode at one end which receives the image projected by a lens outside the tube. A special electrode produces a field which moves the electron image along the length of the tube towards the aperture.

The scanning aperture of the image dissector must be very small to ensure good definition of the picture and so the output signal

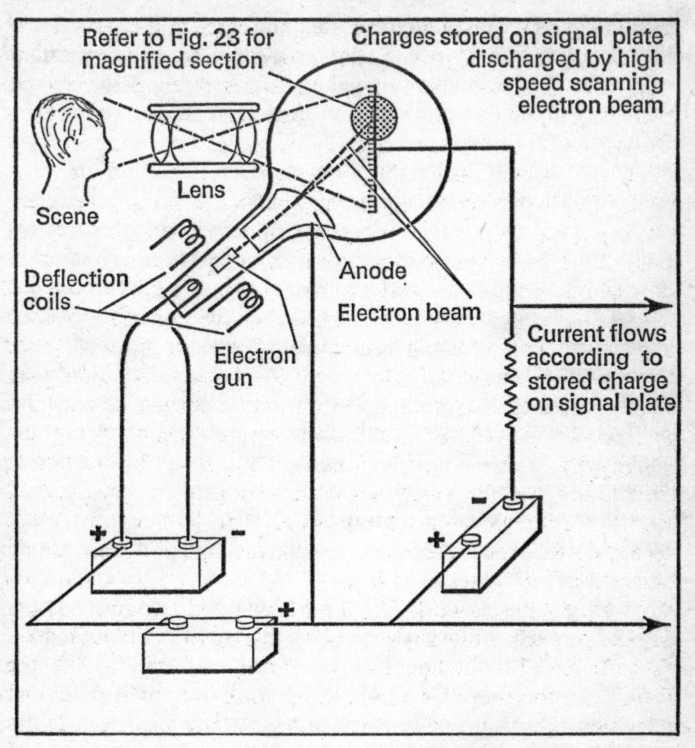


*Figure 22.* Simplified diagram showing principle of iconoscope.

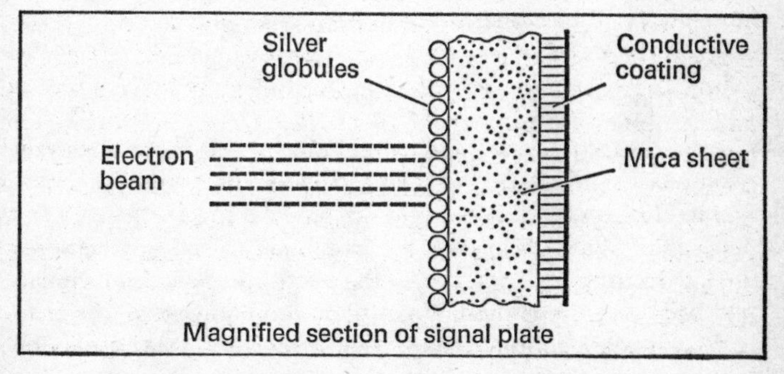


*Figure 23.* Magnified section of iconoscope signal plate.

resulting from the limited number of electrons which pass through this aperture is very weak. Farnsworth's method of overcoming this deficiency was highly original and resulted in a device which was to prove more important than the image dissector itself – the electron multiplier.

We have already dealt with two methods of obtaining free electrons in electron devices: thermionic emission and photoelectric emission. A third way is by secondary emission, which makes use of the effect that if an accelerated electron is propelled at a suitable positively charged metal surface, several secondary electrons are ejected from the surface. Farnsworth placed an array of small anodes inside his image dissector tube so that the electrons progressed and multiplied from one to the next, each succeeding anode having a higher voltage than its predecessor. In this way the relatively small number of electrons passing through the aperture and striking the first anode finally emerged at the other end of the array multiplied thousands of times.

Farnsworth succeeded in getting financial backing for his inventions and his company won most of the inevitable disputes with R.C.A. over patents which followed; but he found the role of an inventive David defying an industrial Goliath too exhausting and retired from the battlefield in 1940, at the age of thirty-four, to a farm in Maine where he built his own small laboratory. His life illustrates the fact that the lone inventor is now at a great disadvantage compared to teams of research workers, but his inventions represent a very great contribution to television, and his electron multiplier ranks as one of the most important contributions to electronics and to modern technology.

## 1939–49

Before 1939 the adjective 'electronic' was used almost exclusively by physicists and referred to the electron and its properties rather than to electron devices. 'Electronics' came into general use after the Second World War as the name given to the applications, outside the main field of radio, of the electronic devices which had then been produced: thermionic tubes and photocells. The electronics industry, conceived in peacetime research, was born in the blast of war and has grown in vigour and size ever since.

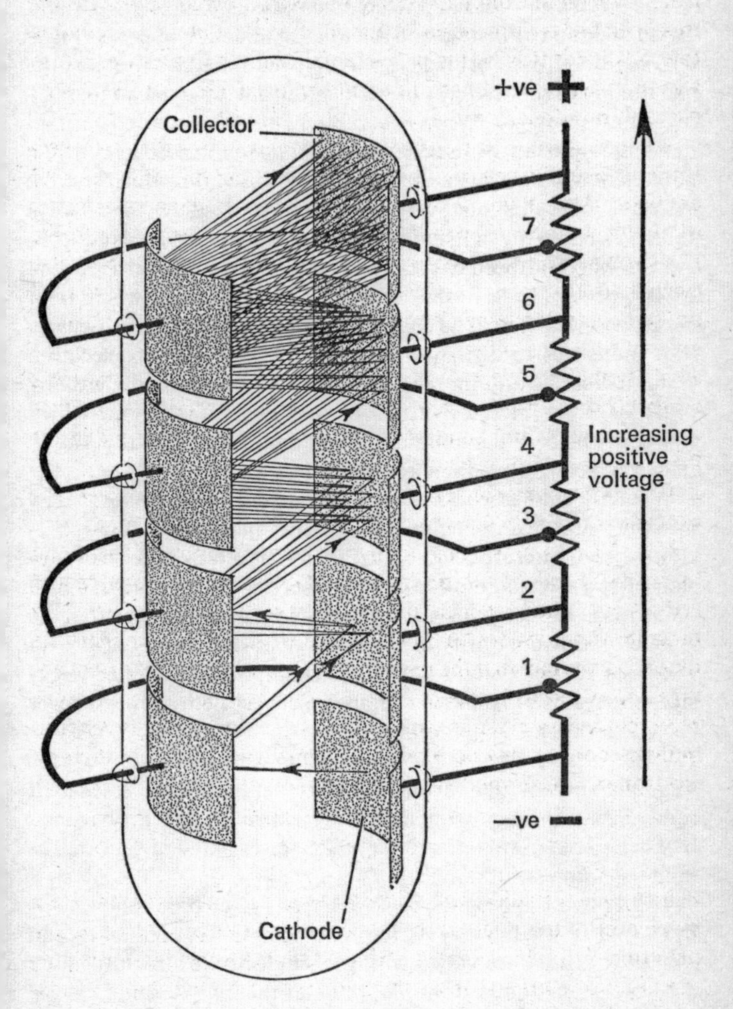


*Figure 24.* The diagram illustrates the mode of action of the electron photomultiplier

The electrical, radio and telephone industries of Germany and Japan and then of Britain and America, and finally of every industrial nation in the world, were turned over more and more to the technology of modern war in which electronics played an increasingly important part. When governments and generals had grasped the vital importance of science and technology in modern war the process of squandering scientific man power and resources in the indiscriminate slaughter, which had characterized the First World War, was reversed. In Britain many engineers, scientists and technicians who had been called up for military training in 1939 and 1940 were sent back to the laboratories and factories where their efforts counted most. The Germans had already geared their peacetime industries to their war machine but the savage persecution of Jews, liberals and free-thinkers by the Nazis robbed Germany of many of her finest scientists, whose contributions to the Allied war effort helped to maintain the lead established by the Allies in radar, fire-control and nuclear weapons.

When the immense resources of the United States began to flow into the production of equipment for communication, radar, fire-control, anti-aircraft devices, etc., there was a tremendous expansion of the electronics industry in America which, together with the British lead in research at the beginning of the war, ensured the technological superiority of the Allies. The discoveries of British scientists in electronics, especially in radar, were developed intensively by teams of American engineers on a scale which had never been approached in peacetime.

While electronics was put to work for the logistics of war, for weapons and counter-weapons, governments on both sides used radio broadcasting to an increasing extent in the propaganda battle, and the telephone networks were essential to civil as well as military administration.

The demands put on the performance of electronic components by the military led to very big improvements in their reliability and efficiency. Miniature valves with robust electrode structures were designed and produced in quantity and there were generally big advances in the techniques of mass production of thermionic tubes and related components. The air forces of the combatant powers used large amounts of electronic equipment and instruments and the search for light-weight materials for such equipment took on all the urgency of the battles in the air. In the latter part of the war the necessity for the rapid solution of the complex problems in fire-control, naval gunnery, ballistics and weapon guidance led to the design of the first electronic computers.

The research, development, production and testing of nuclear weapons and the delivery of the two atom bombs on Hiroshima and Nagasaki would not have been possible without electronics and electronic instruments.

By the end of the war America and Britain had built up massive industrial resources and 'know-how' for the mass production of electronic equipment. Many thousands of trained and experienced scientists, engineers and service technicians had been schooled in war-time electronics. By the end of the nineteen forties electronics had become not only an industry but also a recognized career for science and engineering graduates.

### RADAR AND THE MAGNETRON

Radar – the name was coined by the U.S. Navy from RAdio Detection And Ranging – was one of the main factors in the rapid growth of electronics during and since the last war. Its distant origins can be traced back to 1904, when Professor R. Fessenden of Pittsburgh University used pulses of wireless oscillations for depth sounding, but the immediate prelude to its development was the use of radio waves, by Sir Edward Appleton in Britain and by teams from the Carnegie Foundation in America, to determine the heights of the various layers of the ionosphere (see page 101).

The principle of radar is simple: a beam of energy in the form of waves is directed at an object and the time required for the reflected waves to return to the sender is measured; if the speed of the waves is known the distance of the object can be calculated. By using more than one sender, or a beam whose direction can be precisely fixed, the position as well as the range of the object can be determined. This is all very straightforward for a large fixed object like a cliff a few miles away from a ship: sailors have long used the method of firing a shot in the direction of such a target and measuring the time of arrival of the echo with a stop-watch, allowing about 10 seconds for the sound to go and return a distance of 1 mile. But if the target happens to be an aircraft travelling at, say, 500 m.p.h.

and about 10 miles away, the use of sound waves is out of the question. It would require something like a volcanic eruption to produce a sound powerful enough to have a detectable echo from an aircraft 10 miles away, and the structure for focusing the sound so that the echoes were confined to those from the aircraft would have to be several miles across. Even if some fantastic scheme along these lines were devised it would not be very useful for aircraft detection since there would be a delay of at least 100 seconds before the return of the echo, in which time the aircraft would have moved some 10 miles from its original position whence the sound was dispatched.

Radar systems employ electromagnetic waves which travel with the speed of light, but they still have to solve some formidable engineering problems. Robert Watson-Watt, who led a team of British scientists in the thirties, continued the work of Appleton, at first with continuous radio waves and later with pulsed waves. The thermionic triode oscillators at his disposal could provide only a few watts at the high frequencies (short wavelengths) necessary, and since less than a million-millionth of the power transmitted was returned to the sender from the sort of target of interest it needed a very sensitive receiver to detect the echo. The time of return for waves travelling at 186,000 miles per second is only a few millionths of a second and this time was measured electronically using a cathode-ray oscilloscope (see page 66). The transmitting aerials were mounted on tall towers and chains of these were set up at strategic positions along the south and east coasts of England. It was a remarkable achievement for the British team to have a working radar system ready by the outbreak of war to detect the approach of enemy bombers, and its decisive influence on the Battle of Britain and hence on the course of the war is well known.

When the Luftwaffe began its night-bombing over Britain it became clear that airborne radar was necessary to enable night fighters to detect, intercept and close with the bombers. The ground radar technique, already stretched to its limit, was useless for this purpose since the aerials, whose size is physically related to the wavelength, were much too large to be mounted on aircraft. Smaller aerials meant shorter wavelengths, i.e. higher frequencies. A device was needed to provide very powerful bursts of very high frequency waves. Such a device had been invented in Britain in

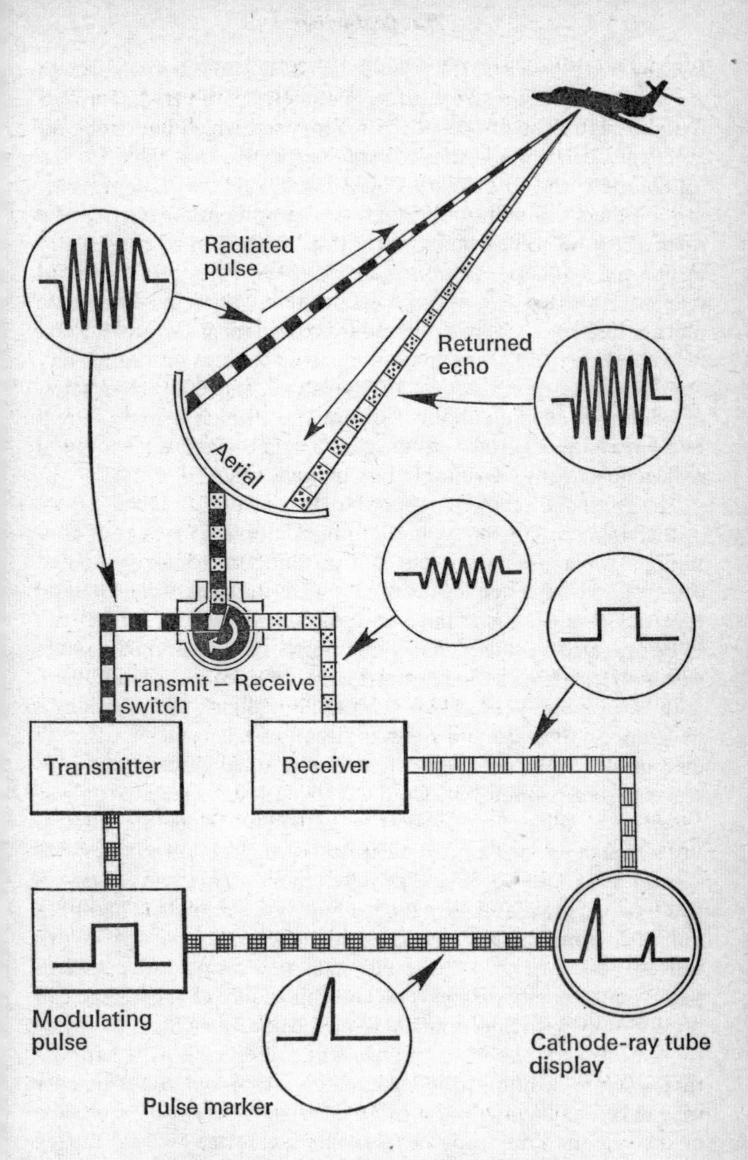


*Figure 25*. The main elements of a radar system.

1939 by two physicists, J. T. Randall and H. A. H. Boot. This was the multicavity magnetron: a thermionic 'tube' of very unconventional design. The anode of the magnetron, which had to be an excellent electrical and thermal conductor, was machined from a solid copper rod to provide a cylindrically symmetrical array of resonant cavities with a tungsten wire cathode in the centre. The sides of the machined block were sealed with discs of copper and in operation it was positioned between the poles of a powerful magnet. As there was also a high positive voltage on the anode block the electrons were subjected to crossed magnetic and electric fields and their resulting gyrations in the cavities produced very high frequency oscillations, of the order of 3,000 megacycles/second or wavelength about 10 centimetres, which were picked up by a wire loop, inserted into the magnetron through a glass-metal seal, and sent into a suitable line or waveguide.

The original 6-segment copper-block valve of Randall and Boot at Birmingham University had produced about 150 watts of continuous wave oscillation but the introduction of oxide-coated cathodes, with the help of the research laboratories of the General Electric Co. and British Thomson-Houston, allowed the magnetron to be operated in pulses, and short bursts of 10 centimetre waves with power as high as 50 kilowatts were obtained in the laboratory.

In September 1940, when submarine sinkings of Allied ships were on the increase and the war situation was critical, a British mission headed by Sir Henry Tizard went to America bearing the secret tube in a small box. On 6 October 1940 the magnetron was tested in the Whippany Laboratory of the Bell Telephone Laboratories and produced a peak pulse output of 10 kilowatts at a frequency of about 3,000 megacycles/second. This was a power five times as great and a frequency four times as high as had been obtained from the best available high-frequency triodes! Work started immediately on the development of airborne radar systems based on the cavity magnetron. The importance of the magnetron may be judged from a comment from the book *One Story of Radar* by A. L. Rowe, one of the pioneers of radiolocation: 'I suppose that few in a position to judge would hesitate to name the cavity magnetron as having had a more decisive effect on the outcome of the war than any other single scientific device evolved during the war. It was of far more importance than the atomic bomb,

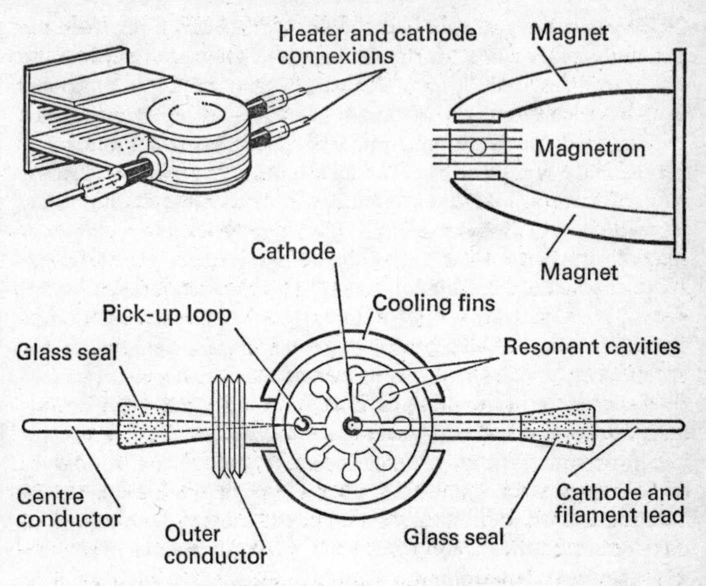


*Figure 26.* Construction of a magnetron.

which had no effect at all on the outcome of the German war and contributed rather to the shortening of the Japanese war than to its result.'

Important as the magnetron was in the war, we are more concerned in this chapter with its effect on the development of electronics and this was very great. University and industrial laboratories in Britain and America cooperated in an unprecedented effort in the development of microwave radar which the magnetron had made possible. The famous Radiation Laboratory of Massachusetts Institute of Technology was formed in November 1940 for work on radar and by the end of the war was employing thousands of scientists and engineers and had produced no less than 28 bulky volumes dealing with its work, a veritable bible for the post-war generation of radar engineers.

The design and fabrication of magnetrons led to a general advance in the theory and practice of electronics. The magnetrons themselves demanded new materials and new high vacuum techniques. Remarkable new magnetic alloys were invented for the powerful but compact permanent magnets which provided the strong magnetic fields for the magnetrons. The need to switch the magnetrons on and off in millionths of a second for pulsed radar led to the development of new high-voltage electronic switches such as the hydrogen thyratron. Since the microwaves generated by magnetrons cannot be carried along ordinary wire connexions without serious loss, interference and distortion, a whole new technology of waveguides was created. Tremendous development took place in cathode-ray tubes, the basis of the radarscope display system, which also amounted to a whole new technology. Special valves, such as klystrons, were developed for the extremely sensitive receivers. The non-active components associated with the purely electronic devices – the transformers, attenuators, resistors, capacitors, etc. – were made to much more stringent specifications for pulse operation and general reliability. As the 'hardware' improved so did the circuit techniques, the measuring techniques and the overall efficiency and performance of the radar systems.

In the twenty years since the end of the war the rapid development of radar for peacetime applications has proceeded in parallel with the military development. Many examples of such applications will be found in this book.

## TRANSISTORS AND SEMICONDUCTOR DEVICES

All the electron devices which we have considered so far operate with free electrons in vacuo (in practice, this means with traces of gas present) or in the presence of gases at low pressures. In these devices the behaviour of electrons, moving under the influence of electric and magnetic fields which could be accurately defined, and relatively unaffected by the nuclear forces from atoms, was well understood after half a century of theory and practice. However, devices consisting of solid pieces of crystalline material which allowed alternating current to flow more readily in one direction than the other were known long before the invention of the thermionic valve. The crystal set which became so well known in the early days of radio depended on the rectifying action at the point of contact between the surface of certain crystals and a fine wire. Crystal valves, using silicon crystals, were found to be more efficient rectifiers for the very high frequency signals reaching radar receivers than any thermionic valves available before the war. The action of these devices was not understood, but they were all made from materials which we now classify as semiconductors: substances which let electric current pass through them more easily than insulators do but much less easily than do true conductors. And although these semiconductor devices had been used as rectifiers, no one had ever succeeded in obtaining *amplification* with them. Until 1948.

In that year John Bardeen and Walter Brattain of the Bell Telephone Laboratories invented the point-contact transistor and William Shockley, who was also working at Bell Laboratories, invented the junction transistor shortly after. These inventions were far from being lucky accidents; they came after various attempts had been made at solid amplifier devices in the previous decade, and were based on theoretical advances in solid state physics extending over fifty years. Bardeen, Brattain and Shockley were engaged on theoretical and experimental studies of the control of the resistance of a layer of semiconductor material by applying electric fields strong enough to penetrate the surface, when they found that if they placed two suitable contacts on the surface close together and a third common electrode elsewhere on the surface, the current flow between one contact and the common electrode could be influenced by the current through the other contact. Under suitable conditions feeble variations in one current could produce much stronger variations in the other.

The point-contact transistor uses a small wafer of crystalline germanium – a typical semiconductor with some metallic and some non-metallic properties – on the surface of which two pointed wire contacts are positioned close together. One is called the emitter and the other, the collector; their functions are similar to those of cathode and anode in a thermionic valve. A third contact, called the base contact, is made on the opposite surface of the wafer with a much larger area of contact. This device can be used to amplify small currents but it never really emerged from the laboratory stage mainly because its construction limited very severely the currents which it could handle.

The real importance of the point-contact transistor was that it demonstrated the possibilities of the practical application of electron flow in crystals and provided the experimental basis upon

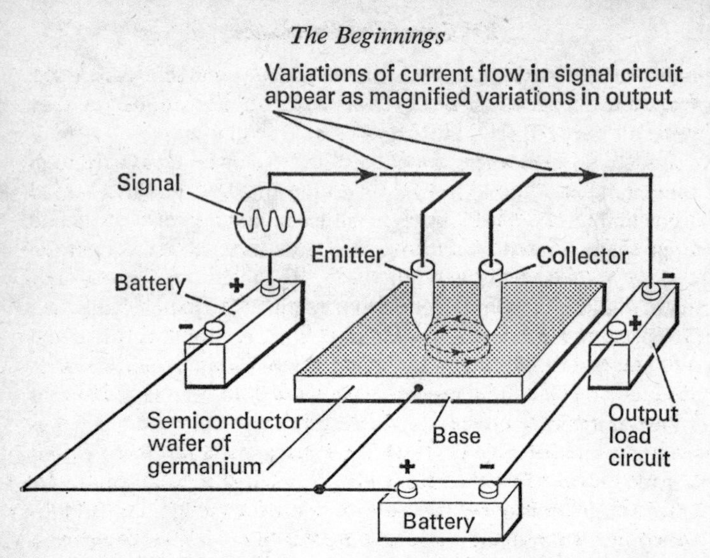


*Figure 27.* Simplified diagram to show how a point-contact transistor amplifies a signal.

which Shockley and others developed the theory of junction transistors – a theory which predicted accurately the properties of the first devices which were made two years later. Some appreciation of the theory of transistors may be gained from a (very elementary) consideration of the properties of semiconductors.

The electrical characteristics of semiconductors, which we have already seen fall between those of insulators and those of conductors, depend on their crystal structure. The most commonly used for transistors are silicon and germanium, elements which are in the same chemical group as carbon and which assume the diamond's crystalline structure: a highly symmetrical arrangement of atoms in which each atom is surrounded by four others equidistant from it, positioned at alternate corners of a cube. The forces holding the atoms together arise from the sharing of electrons between atoms and carbon, silicon and germanium are alike in that they have four electrons available for sharing. In crystals of these substances each atom therefore forms four bonds with its four neighbours, each bond comprising two shared electrons. If the crystal is perfect every electron is tightly bound and is not available for electronic conduction; the crystal is therefore an insulator. To make it useful for transistors and semiconductor devices we deliberately spoil its perfection by introducing a very small number of certain foreign atoms.

If, for example, a very small trace of arsenic is introduced into a pure germanium crystal a few arsenic atoms replace germanium atoms in the crystal lattice. Now arsenic has five electrons in its outer shell and since only four of these are required for the four co-valent bonds of the germanium lattice, one is left free to roam through the lattice. Like the conduction electrons in metals the surplus arsenic electrons acquire the energy to move through the material and this amounts to flow of current and therefore the germanium crystal conducts. This type of conduction is called n-type because it depends on the negative charges of the electrons; the crystal is then of n-type material; the arsenic impurity, which need represent only a few parts in a million, is called a donor impurity.

On the other hand if the impurity is a substance like gallium, which has three electrons to share, it is short of one electron to complete the four bonds. It obtains the extra electron from a completed bond leaving a 'hole'. This hole, which can be likened to a bubble in water, can be transferred through the lattice in much the same way as an electron is transferred but its effect is that of a movement of positive charge instead of a negative. This is positive or p-type conduction; the material is p-type material; the impurity is called an acceptor impurity.

We thus have a technique for making the semiconductor conduct in two ways using either positive or negative charge carriers. A typical procedure for making a junction transistor would be as follows: a germanium crystal is grown from a melt of extremely pure germanium to which has been added a measured trace of arsenic. This produces n-type material and an n-type crystal is slowly drawn from the melt. At a certain point a measured amount of gallium is dropped in the melt, sufficient to compensate for the arsenic and leave enough over to produce a calculated amount of acceptor impurity. As the growing crystal continues to be extracted from the melt it changes from n-type to p-type and, since the crystal is grown vertically, there will be a horizontal junction between the two types. Alternating layers of n- or p-type material can be produced as required by appropriate additions of impurities. The raw material for production of junction transistors is a

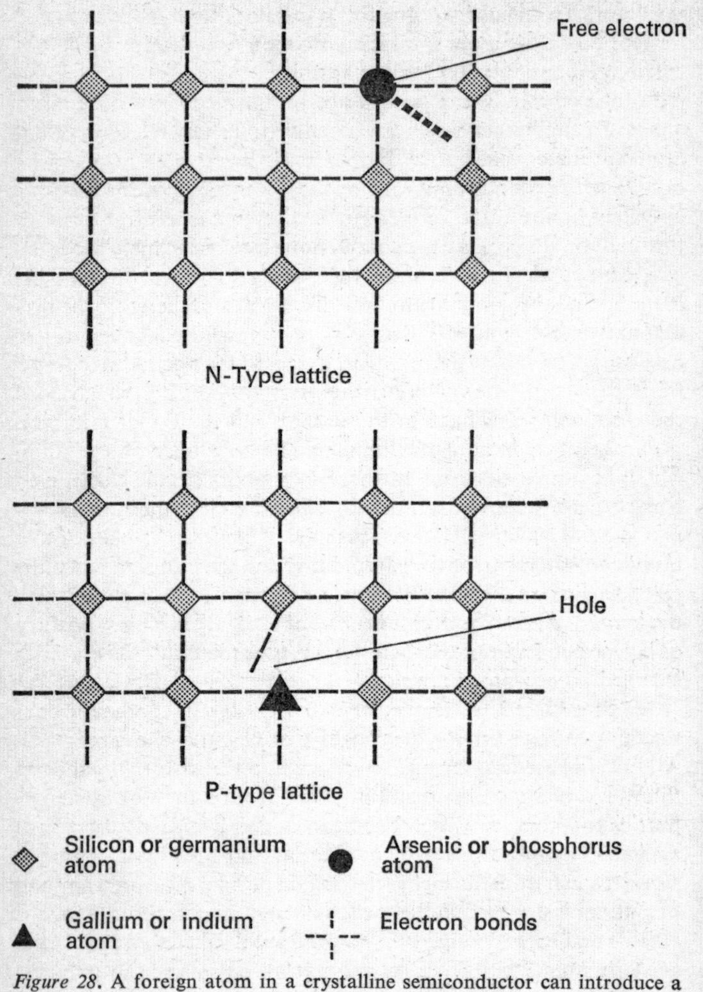


*Figure 28.* A foreign atom in a crystalline semiconductor can introduce a free electron or a hole.

suitable slice through the finished crystal containing an n–p junction followed by a p–n junction. A typical slice, say 2 inches square and $\frac{1}{8}$ inch thick will be cut and diced by diamond saws into many hundreds of tiny bars $\frac{1}{8}$ inch long, each being a sandwich of a p-region between two n-regions. Leads are attached to each of these regions: the p-region is called the base and the n-regions, the collector and emitter.

For a detailed description of the theory of action of junction transistors the reader is referred to the bibliography; the thing I want to emphasize here is that this action depends on the movement of the two kinds of charge carriers – electrons and holes – across the boundary regions between n- and p-type semiconductors. In the technology of practically all transistors and semiconductor devices the provision of these accurately controlled boundary regions is all-important.

The invention of transistors and solid-state devices led to an acceleration in the growth of electronics. In the decade 1950–60 very large amounts of capital were invested by the leading industrial nations in the research, development and production programmes for transistors and semiconductor devices. In the United States, in particular, transistors were considered to be essential for the defence programme, and the Government provided massive financial support to electronics firms which secured a decisive lead for the Americans over the rest of the world. Why were these new devices so important and why are they steadily replacing their older equivalents? A brief review of their advantages compared with thermionic devices will provide the answers to these questions.

Transistors are made from parts which do not wear out. Even the best thermionic valves slowly deteriorate because of atomic changes in their cathodes and slow leaks in their evacuated or gas-filled envelopes. When transistors were first produced in the 1950s engineers found them unreliable and erratic but this was found to be due to lack of experience and care in their design, manufacture and use. The materials and processes involved in the manufacture of transistors demand standards of purity and precision which are hardly equalled in any other product. For example, completely new methods had to be worked out to measure impurities in processed crystals of the order of one part in a hundred million. But once the need was understood the necessary advances in technology for the production of reliable transistors were soon achieved. They now have a virtually unlimited life.

Transistors waste very little power. They require no heating to

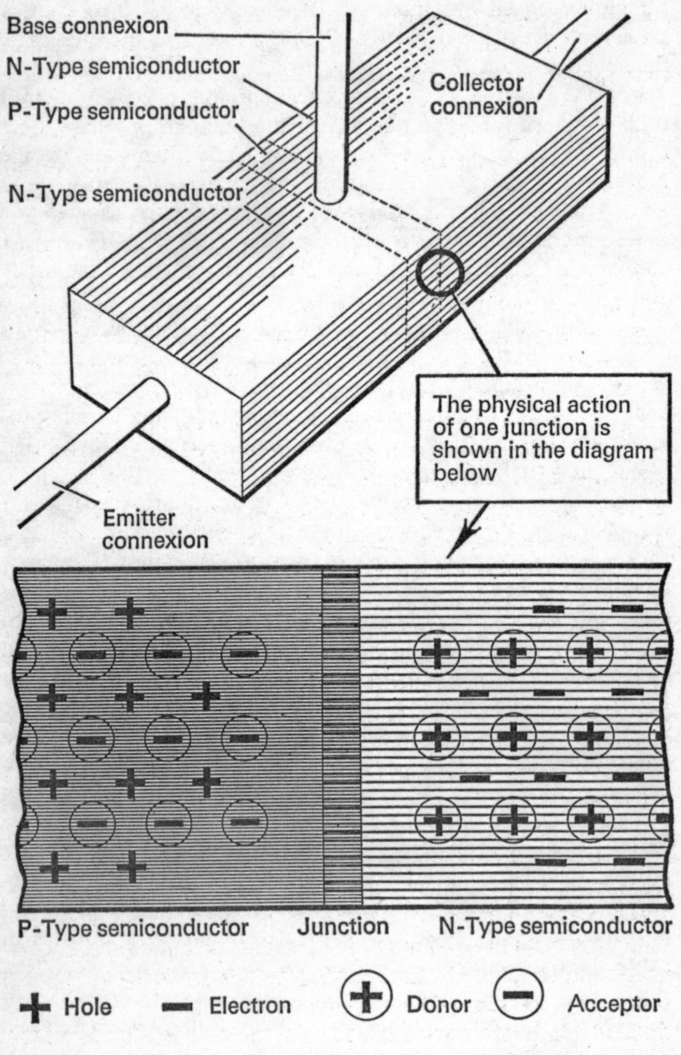


*Figure 29.* Basic structure of an N-P-N junction transistor.

generate their free electrons and small low-capacity batteries are adequate to maintain their operation. This means that equipment made with transistors is more efficient, lighter, more portable and runs cooler than comparable valve equipment.

Since no heating is required there is no delay in transistor equipment waiting for things to warm up, as there is with thermionic valves. This is a great advantage with 'entertainment' equipment, such as radio and television receivers, and it may be vital with some kinds of measuring or recording equipment.

Transistors, like other solid-state devices, can be made very robust, with great resistance to shock and vibration; this is both difficult and expensive to achieve with valves or mechanical devices. Their very small size and weight, combined with low heat dissipation, permits very high density packing of components and, in combination with their reliability, this has made possible the design of the very compact but intricate circuits which are essential for such applications as computers, portable measuring instruments, satellite instrumentation, etc.

The transformation of electronic computers from monstrous laboratory machines requiring constant skilled maintenance into efficient and reliable industrial and commercial equipment was due mainly to the introduction of transistors and solid-state devices. The huge and cumbersome computers of the fifties – such as ENIAC with no less than 18,000 valves – had reached the limit of what was possible with thermionic valves and conventional components; they spent more time out of commission due to failure of parts than they did in useful work. The greatly increased reliability, compactness and efficiency of transistors compared with valves was the main factor in making possible the 'second generation' of computers which put the computer industry on its feet.

Most of the disadvantages and deficiencies of transistors which loomed so large in their early life of ten years ago have disappeared with increased research, plant investment, and know-how. Advances in the theory of the solid state have gone hand in hand with advances in the practical techniques of growing and processing crystals, of micro-manipulation and quantity production of miniature assemblies to close tolerances. In ten years a variety of types of transistor appeared, with greatly increased frequency range, speed of operation, voltage, current and power rating and with steadily decreasing size and cost. The growth in the output of transistors has to some extent been at the expense of valves, but it is still doubtful whether valves will eventually be entirely replaced. There are still no solid-state devices capable of replacing high-power valve transmitters or comparable to cathode ray tubes. Moreover, most transistors are liable to be damaged by high temperatures and nuclear radiation and this poses problems in instrumentation for space exploration and for nuclear power stations.

Transistors have received a good deal of publicity mainly because of their widespread use in 'entertainment' radio, but they form only one branch of a much larger, but less widely known, family of semiconductor devices. The growing demand for better and cheaper transistors led to rapid advances in theoretical knowledge and production technology of all semiconductor devices. Other branches of the semiconductor family are: varistors, which include the ubiquitous little diodes which have almost entirely replaced thermionic diodes and are now made by the million; solid-state photoelectric devices, including phototransistors and photomultipliers; thermistors, used extensively for temperature compensation and measurement and as non-linear circuit elements; ferro-electric and ferrite devices for magnetic memories in computers and for microwave components; and thermoelectric devices which can be used to convert heat directly into electricity or as the basis of refrigerators with no moving parts.

Some idea of the growth in the volume and value of production of semiconductor devices in the 1950–60 decade may be gained from the figures for the total national production of these devices in the U.S.A. This increased from about five million dollars (mainly for the telephone industry) in 1950 to more than 300 million dollars in 1960. A similar rate of expansion, but starting at a much lower absolute level, can be observed in Britain, France, West Germany, Italy and Japan.

## FROM MINIATURIZATION TO MICRO-ELECTRONICS

The demands for reduction in size and weight of electronic equipment and components, which were pressed vigorously by the military from 1939 onwards, did not slacken after the war. Small, light, components were desirable for portable radios or airborne equipment; they were essential for equipment such as large digital computers, containing thousands of components, if it was not to become unmanageable and uneconomic. Transistors, and other semiconductor devices, meant a big step in the direction of miniaturization: not only were they much smaller than miniature valves, but in addition they dispensed with much bulky auxiliary equipment, such as heater transformers, associated with valves. With their introduction into electronic equipment there was added incentive to reduce the size of the 'passive' components associated with them, such as resistors and capacitors. Much research and development went into reducing the size of such components without sacrificing their performance or reliability.

Printed circuit techniques marked another stage in this general evolution towards smaller, more compact and more reliable equipment. In these, solid wire connexions to individual components were replaced by printed connexions on a flat circuit board to which the components were soldered. Some types of components were printed as well as the connexions between them. The usual process starts with a board of insulating material which is coated with copper (or other metallic conductor) and the portions of the metal which represent wiring and components are given a protective coat, using photographic methods. The unit is then immersed in acid which removes the unprotected metal, leaving the circuit elements. A packing density of the order of 30 components per cubic inch was achieved with these methods and the use of solid-state devices, compared with about 10 per cubic inch with sub-miniature valves and conventional assemblies.

The next step can be described as the 'Micromodule' technique. A typical module is a ceramic wafer about 0·3 inches square holding separate miniature components, and many such wafers are stacked one upon another with vertical wires inter-connecting them mechanically and electrically. Packing densities of the order of 100 components per cubic inch are attained.

Next, individual containers for components were dispensed with and transistors and associated components were formed, together with their inter-connexions, *in situ* as thin films on glass or ceramic substrates. The techniques used in these 'integrated circuits' include diffusion, etching, alloying and evaporation. Component densities of the order of 1,000 per cubic inch can be

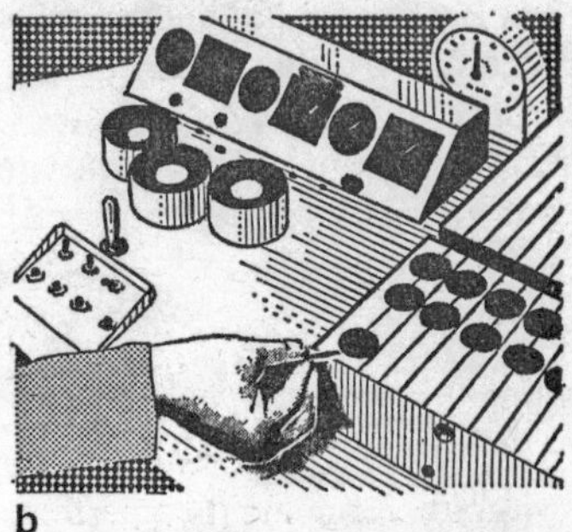


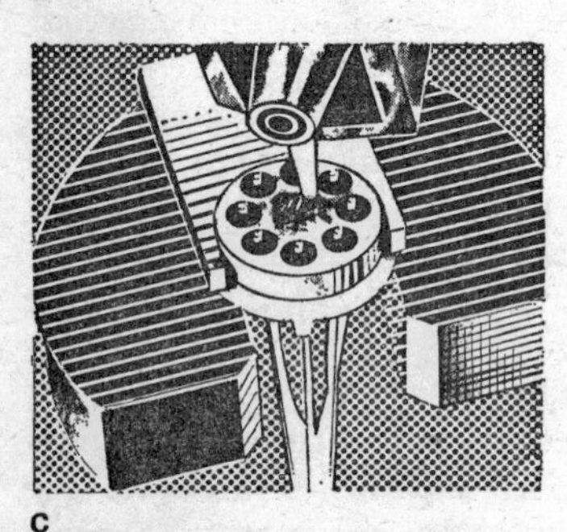

a Master mask

b Slices after photo-resist

c Bonding connecting wires

d Checking with multi-probe tester

e Micromanipulator

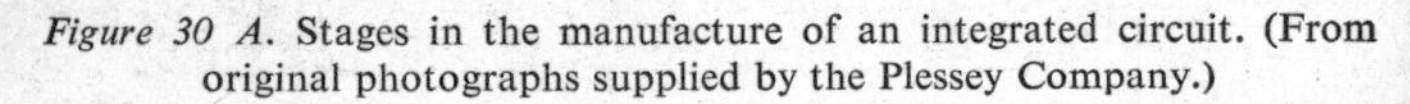

*Figure 30 A*. Stages in the manufacture of an integrated circuit. (From original photographs supplied by the Plessey Company.)

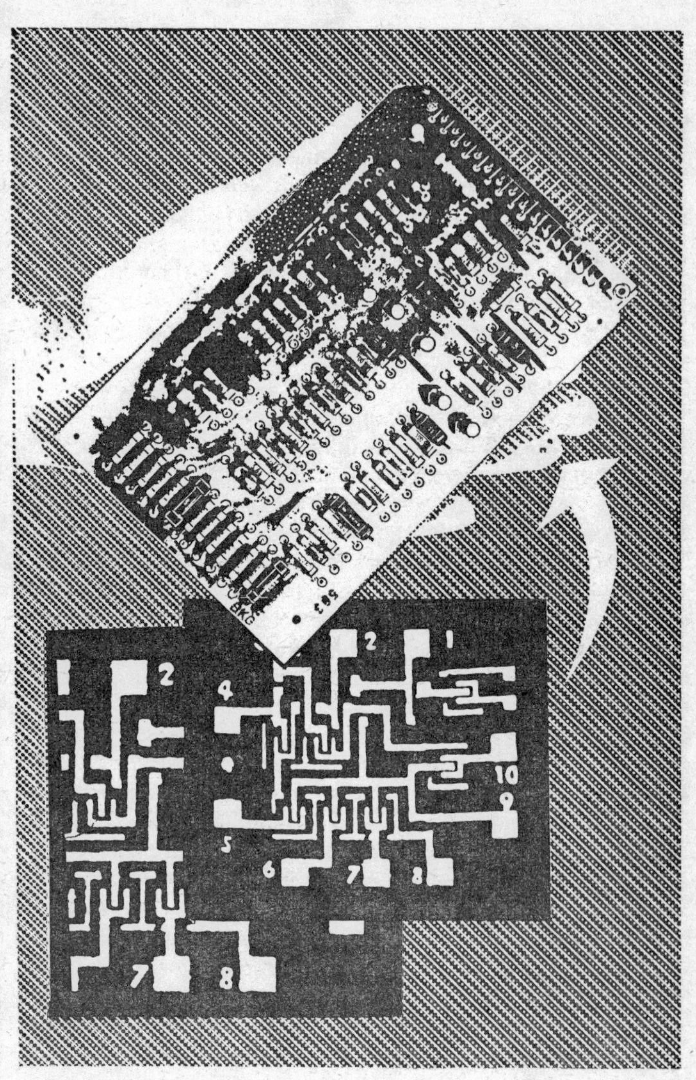


*Figure 30 B.* The two integrated circuits shown on the finger tip (and magnified in the lower part of the diagram) serve the same function as the entire circuit board.

achieved together with greater reliability than with any of the earlier methods.

The latest stage in this progress towards the infinitely small is known as Molecular Electronics. The idea of individual circuit elements is discarded entirely and the desired circuit is built up virtually molecule by molecule from suitable material. The techniques for fashioning these structures include: the vacuum deposition of extremely thin films only a few atoms thick, micro-diffusion, photo-etching, and the use of finely focused electron beams as very precise tools for the fabrication of microscopic circuits. Maximum component density has been increased by another order of magnitude to about 10,000 per cubic inch.

In the last twenty years the packing density of electronic components has been increased one thousand times. Will this be increased a thousand times again in the next twenty years? It is possible that this may happen in much less than twenty years. At the time of writing an attempt is being made at Manchester University to fabricate one hundred passive circuit elements in an area one millimetre square. Assuming that the substrate and interconnexions are not more than one hundredth of an inch thick this could represent a packing density of several millions per cubic inch. This project can only be contemplated because two revolutionary electronic techniques are now available: the machining operations involved will be carried out to an accuracy of about one hundred-thousandth of an inch using an electron beam programmed by the Atlas computer owned by the University.

An even more ambitious project has started at Stanford Research Institute in California with the objective of machining thin films with electron beams into 10,000 million individual areas per square inch. Dr Kenneth Shoulders, who is directing the project, hopes to have a prototype in about two years of a data-processing system in which the component packing density will be of the order of 100,000 million components per cubic inch. Even if only one tenth of this fantastic figure is achieved this would equal the density of nerve cells in a human brain! Advances of this order will lead to electronic devices which will be as far ahead of present-day devices as these are of the pre-electronic machines. The implications of this will be discussed in later chapters but it is not difficult to see that they will rival the marvels of science fiction.

# PART TWO

# The Electronic Revolution

# 4
# The Revolution in Communications

> We are working towards a condition when any two persons on earth will be able to be completely present to one another in not more than 1/24th of a second. We shall never reach it, but that is the limit we shall approach indefinitely.
>
> J. B. S. Haldane: *Daedalus* (*1923*)

PERHAPS the best index of civilization is the level and extent of the facilities for communication at any stage, from the grunts and yells of primitive men to the communication satellites and oceanic cables of today. The history of communication reveals the complex pattern of advancing civilization and in the twentieth century this is interwoven with the pattern of the electronic revolution. In the previous chapter we traced in outline the way in which the search for improved techniques in wireless communication led to the invention of the thermionic valve and so to the birth of electronics. In this chapter we shall see that the revolutionary effect of electronic devices went far beyond the hopes and dreams of their inventors.

## THE ELECTRIC TELEGRAPH

The precursor of the electronic revolution in communications was the mid-nineteenth-century revolution brought about by the electromagnetic telegraph. The fact that electric current travelled along wire conductors at speeds approaching that of light, and that it deflected a magnetic compass near the wires, inevitably suggested a method of rapid signalling to the enthusiastic amateurs who dabbled with electricity in the early nineteenth century. Many and wonderful were the devices which they invented to transmit and detect the electric signals. Those which survived the nineteenth century included: the first electro-magnet, the electric bell, the pencil recorder, the Morse key and the typewriting telegraph.

Inventors such as Morse in America and Wheatstone in Britain were motivated by the demands of the rapidly developing railways and by the money value of the swift transmission of news which might affect the prices of goods and stocks. Morse invented a simple relay to repeat signals automatically from one section of a line to the next, and this made it possible to open a line 40 miles long for public business in 1839.

The electric telegraph was very successful for short lines but it was not easy to get good results over long lines. The first satisfactory transatlantic cable linking the City and Wall Street, which was laid in 1866, required all the experience and ingenuity of the great physicist, Lord Kelvin, and all the resources of the Anglo-American Telegraph Company of which he was a director. This cable, when it was finally completed, was the high point of applied science for its time: Kelvin invented both his mirror galvanometer and syphon recorder in the course of his research in connexion with it. Yet though powerful companies like Anglo-American and Western Union continued to build up their investments in telegraph lines the research was not continued and the telegraph industry was content to grow fat on the proceeds of a world-wide telegraph traffic which it had developed by 1900. It failed dismally to appreciate the importance of the work on the telephone by Bell and later on the 'wireless' by Marconi. Both these inventors had to find new backers and set up new companies, but even if they had been smothered by the vested telegraph interests the obvious advantages of the 'talking telegraph' and communication without wires could not have been withheld from the public for long.

## THE TELEPHONE

If the people of the nineteenth century were impressed by the transmission of electric signals along telegraph wires one can imagine their reactions on first hearing a human voice transmitted in this way. The success of the telephone was immediate and assured, although it was the climax of more than forty years of effort and there were some very near misses before Alexander Graham Bell produced a device in 1876 which conveyed sound electrically. Bell realized that he had to convert the variations in the density of the air which are caused by human speech into sympathetic variations in electric current. His 'microphone' consisted of a speaking tube leading to a flat disc mounted close to a coil of wire which was connected to a battery. When the sound waves struck the disc it vibrated in sympathy and set up corresponding variations in the current through the coil, and these variations were transmitted along the wire to a similar device at the receiving end, where the reverse process occurred.

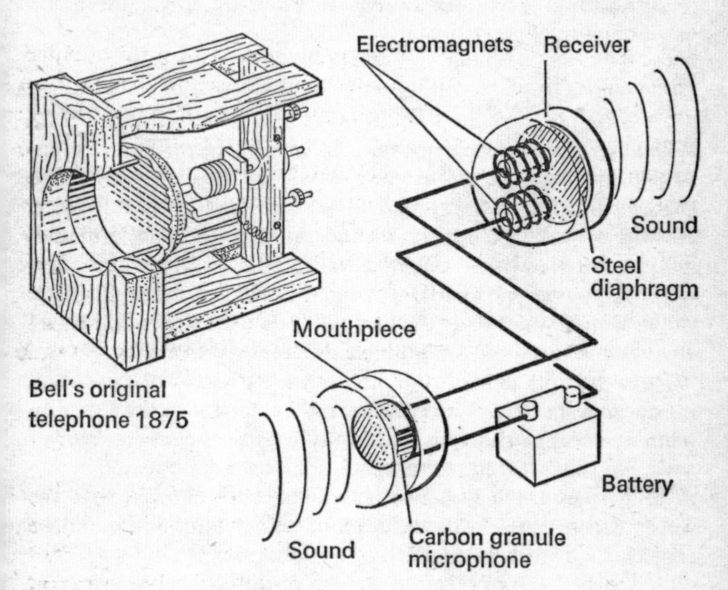


*Figure 31.* Principle of the telephone.

People who grumble about the poor intelligibility on modern telephones would be very unhappy indeed with Bell's original equipment but it was quite good enough to found the telephone industry. When Bell and his backers failed to sell his patents to Western Union they set up their own company in 1877 to license the construction of telephone lines by independent groups, and lease telephone instruments to them. Bell did not repeat the mistake of the telegraph industry in neglecting research. He started a laboratory in Boston in 1876 which was to develop into the Bell Telephone Laboratories, now one of the finest industrial research organizations in the world, and one which was to play a big part in the development of telecommunications and electronics. The telephone network developed rapidly in the United States and Europe but less rapidly in Britain until the Government transferred the system from a private monopoly to the Post Office in 1912. But the really explosive development of telephone communication on a world scale had to await the invention of the valve amplifier and radio.

## COMMUNICATION WITHOUT WIRES

When the great German physicist Heinrich Hertz first demonstrated the existence of 'wireless waves' in 1888 he had not the slightest interest in any practical application for his discovery. He was providing the experimental proof of the purely mathematical theory, worked out with uncanny insight by Clerk Maxwell twenty-five years earlier, of the existence of electromagnetic waves which would obey the same laws as light waves and travel at the same speed but would have different wavelengths.

Hertz set up a pair of rods, each with a knob at one end, and produced a spark discharge between the knobs with the aid of an induction coil. A short distance away he placed a similar pair of rods, *not connected to the first pair*, and a spark appeared across these whenever the first pair sparked. Hertz showed that the waves which caused this were about a foot long and could be projected for the whole length of his laboratory.

The early death of Hertz at the age of thirty-seven was a great loss to physical science, and he did not live to see any of the results of his work, but by 1895 Oliver Lodge in Britain, Popov in Russia and Marconi in Italy had used electromagnetic waves as signals. They all used a device called a coherer (see Chapter 3), invented by Professor E. Branly of France, as a detector of the waves.

It was Guglielmo Marconi, son of a wealthy Italian family, who first saw the practical possibilities of wireless waves. He read about Hertz's experiments in an Italian electrical journal, and became inspired with the idea of communication without wires. Although he was not a trained scientist he transformed the top floor of his parents' villa into a laboratory where he spent his time constructing transmitting apparatus and improving the coherer.

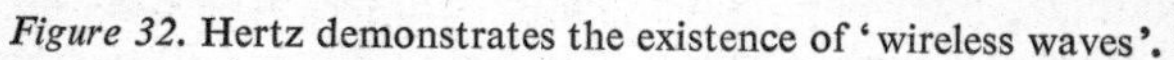


*Figure 32.* Hertz demonstrates the existence of 'wireless waves'.

His family knew all the 'best' people in England and decided that young Guglielmo would have better prospects there, so he arrived in 1896 with introductions to everyone of any importance in the field of telecommunications, including Sir William Preece, chief engineer of the G.P.O. Preece arranged a demonstration for the post office engineers who were very impressed when Marconi showed that messages could be sent for up to eight miles. The British Marconi Company was formed in the following year, when Marconi was only twenty-three, with a capital of £100,000 subscribed by wealthy backers who expected the sensational commercial success of the telephone to be repeated with wireless. Marconi, who was even better at 'selling' wireless than at inventing it, assured the investors that most of the lucrative transatlantic cable business would be captured. He pointed out that a transatlantic cable cost over £1 million to install and over £100,000 to maintain annually, whereas the capital cost of a wireless station which could handle the same amount of traffic would be about £50,000 and its maintenance cost about £12,000 annually.

Alas for the calculations of the promoters, Marconi had not taken into acount the difficulties of long-distance wireless communication (although he had considerable success over comparatively short distances) and the British Marconi Co. paid no dividends from 1897 to 1910. But, as we shall see, the investors' loss was to prove the scientists' gain. The first paid wireless message was sent in 1898 between stations which were erected in Bournemouth and Alum Bay in the Isle of Wight. In the same year wireless telegraphy received the royal blessing when Queen Victoria used it to exchange no less than 150 messages with the Prince of Wales between the Isle of Wight and the Royal yacht *Osborne*. In 1899 messages were sent across the Channel from Chelmsford to Boulogne, a distance of 85 miles.

The first transatlantic wireless message was achieved in 1901: the letter 's' was sent in Morse code from Poldhu, Cornwall and the 'dot-dot-dot' was heard faintly by Marconi and two assistants 1,700 miles away in St John's Newfoundland, where an aerial had been hung from a kite to gain the maximum height. This was a great success for Marconi, particularly as he had refused to be discouraged by the opinion of many scientists of the time that his long distance experiment was bound to fail. These scientists argued that it had been amply demonstrated that wireless waves were electromagnetic waves obeying the same laws as light waves, and therefore they should travel in straight lines. In order for an aerial to be in line of sight with a transmitter some 2,000 miles away on the spherical surface of the earth it would have to be more than 500 miles high, even allowing for some bending of the waves by

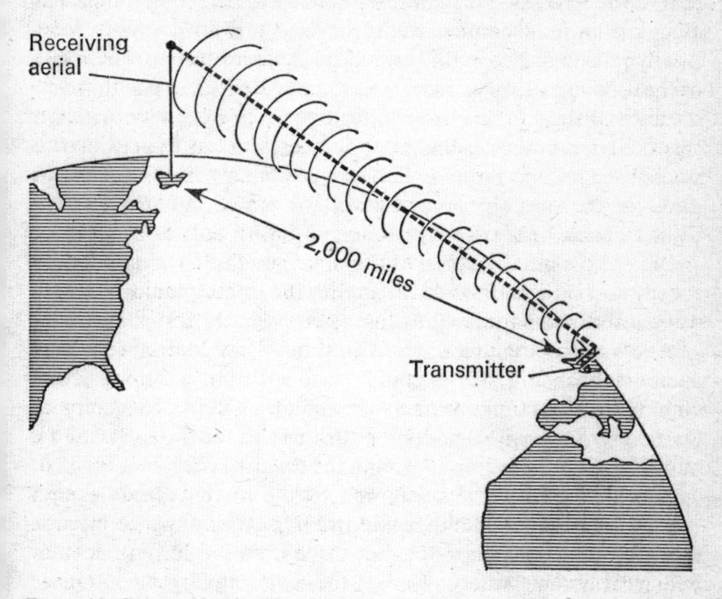


*Figure 33.* Communications on a spherical earth; for direct reception from a transmitter 2,000 miles away the receiving aerial would have to be several hundred miles high.

the earth's atmosphere. Marconi's success made the scientists think again and in 1902 the brilliant English theoretician Oliver Heaviside and the American physicist A. E. Kennelly independently put forward the theory that there was a reflecting layer around the earth and the waves used by Marconi were bounced round the earth between this layer and the sea.

Twenty-three years later Sir Edward Appleton proved the existence not only of the Kennelly–Heaviside layer but also of others above and below it. These layers made up the ionosphere, a region extending from about 55 miles to over 200 miles above the earth's surface consisting of positively charged ions and free electrons. Long distance radio communication is utterly dependent on the ionosphere. It is completely transparent to light waves but becomes more and more opaque as the wavelength of the incident radiation increases. Very short wireless waves are hardly reflected at all, medium waves are partially reflected, and long waves almost totally reflected. The nature and distribution of the various layers of the ionosphere vary in a complex manner with the position and distance of the sun and the relative frequency of sun storms, and this variation makes it difficult to forecast the exact performance of any long-range radio system. Thus Marconi was the first to discover the one big advantage of submarine cable over long distance radio links: that its efficiency can be predicted accurately.

Despite his intial success, Marconi was unable to win the battle for transatlantic communications with the established cable companies and soon found that his best prospects for commercial success lay in communications with ships. The Marconi company soon established a strong commercial position in ship-to-shore communications and contracts for equipping thirty-two ships of the British Navy with Marconi apparatus and for the erection of a number of wireless stations around the English coast were secured. The British example was followed by the merchant navies and battleships of other countries and British Marconi, which insisted that Marconi equipment was not to be used for communication with rival systems, was on the road to a world monopoly. However this pugnacious policy was vigorously challenged by German and American interests and their governments and in 1908 it was agreed that international coastal stations should be opened to all senders.

The sinking of the *Titanic* in 1912 brought home in the most dramatic manner the importance of wireless to the safety of life at sea: although the 700 survivors owed their lives to the response of the *Carpathia* to the S O S signal of the *Titanic* another vessel which was much nearer at the time of the disaster passed by because it was not equipped with wireless. After this, legislation enacted in Britain, America and other maritime nations obliged all ships above a certain size to carry wireless, and from then on the Marconi companies flourished. It is one of the ironies of history that Marconi's early difficulties with long-distance radio aroused interest in the ionosphere, and the methods used to investigate it led to radar which now makes a repetition of the *Titanic* disaster extremely unlikely.

Marconi was committed to spark wireless telegraphy (see Chapter 3) and within the limitations of this rather crude and inefficient method of transmission his research workers made appreciable advances in better tuning, reducing the effects of static and interference which were very bad with the early systems, and attaining greater distances especially with beam transmission. But he failed to see the superiority of continuous wave transmission, and of radio telephony over radio telegraphy. It was left to the Germans to start continuous wave transmission (with machine-generated continuous waves) across the North Atlantic in 1914. The first wireless telephone signals were sent (see Chapter 3) by the American Telephone and Telegraph in 1915. But Marconi's most serious blind spot was in not seeing the revolutionary possibilities of the Fleming diode, for which he had the patents since its invention in 1904, and the application of electronics to wireless communication was left to the Americans long enough for them to establish a head lead.

When electronic devices *were* used by the Marconi group they soon got some remarkable results. During the 1914–18 war all the major belligerents conducted secret research into the new methods of communication. The Marconi group was occupied with the problem of sending messages on wavelengths which could not be intercepted easily by the enemy, and C. S. Franklin was asked by Marconi to see if the short waves originally discovered by Hertz could be adapted for this purpose. Franklin repeated Hertz's experiments in 1916, using thermionic valves and beam transmission, and found that he could get very successful transmission and reception of messages using short waves. Hertz had demonstrated that the waves could be focused and directed with concave mirrors, in much the same way as light waves, and Franklin developed these techniques. The engineering problems were in fact less than with long waves since the dimensions of the mirrors have to be of the same order as the wavelength and long wave reflectors involve very large arrays.

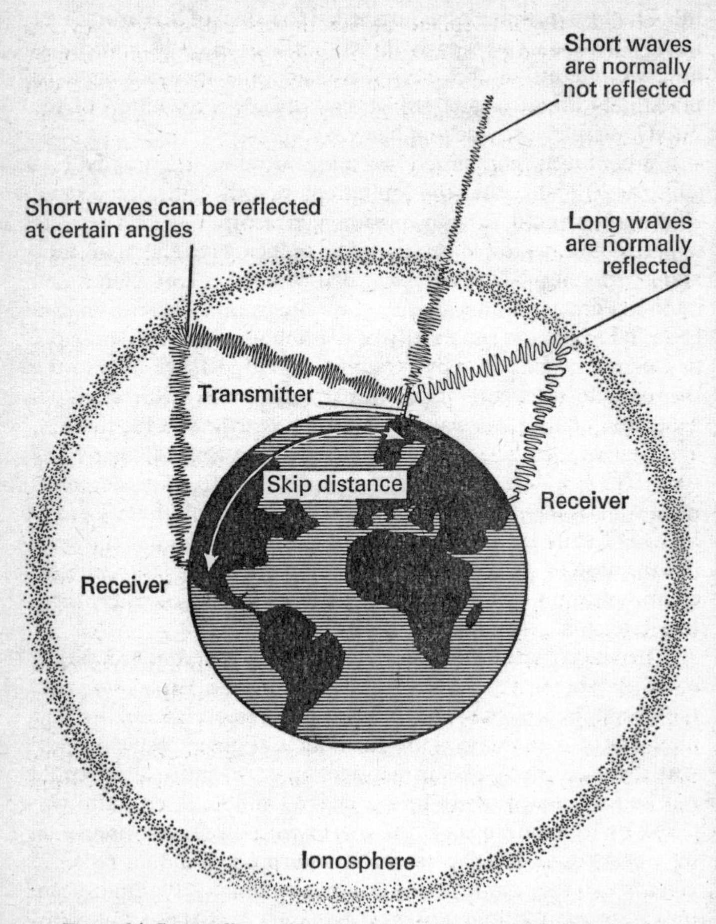


*Figure 34.* Some effects of the ionosphere on long and short waves.

After the war experiments with short waves were continued in Britain and America both by professionals, such as Franklin and the American, Conrad, and by amateurs. The very surprising fact emerged that communication with short waves was possible over very long distances. It appears that if the short waves are directed at the ionosphere at certain critical angles they are reflected back to earth instead of going straight on and can be made to 'skip' round the earth. In 1924 the Post Office awarded a contract to the Marconi Company to erect short-wave stations in Australia, Canada, India and South Africa. The success of these stations induced all other wireless companies to enter the short-wave field and today a world-wide network of beamed short-wave stations provides the radio link between countries and continents which was the only alternative to cable networks until Telstar was rocketed into orbit.

### ELECTRONICS AND LINE COMMUNICATIONS

Between the wars the rapid growth of the radio industry and radio broadcasting supplied the technical means for the improvement and extension of communication by telegraph and telephone cable. Thin copper wires are satisfactory for speech currents provided they are not more than a few miles long, and thick wires can be used for distances up to about 25 miles, but for longer lines the losses in any practicable telephone cable are prohibitive. With electronic amplifiers, similar to those developed for radio circuits, inserted at suitable intervals along the line and at the terminals, the speech signals can be boosted so that economic telephone cable can be used to transmit messages over hundreds of miles. The valve amplifier was the key to the networks of long lines which stretched over the large land masses of the United States, Europe and the Soviet Union and made it possible to telephone from one end of a continent to the other.

Cables and amplifiers for long trunk lines are expensive, and, with increasing traffic, telephone engineers began to look for ways of sending more than one conversation along a single pair of wires. The solution was found in carrier telephony, another technique borrowed from radio. The principle of this is to generate a wide band of frequencies, using valve oscillators, at one end of the line and divide the band into a number of channels each of which takes up no more than about 4,000 cycles width (an adequate bandwidth for satisfactory reproduction of speech) in the spectrum generated. Each channel acts as a carrier on which one conversation is impressed and sent along the line. At the receiving end the different channels are separated, amplified and demodulated, i.e. the speech information is recovered from them. Thousands of miles of trunk telephone cables now use carrier systems to carry 24 separate conversations on each pair of wires, a 12-pair cable thus coping with 288 conversations at once.

To span the seas and oceans either radio links or submarine cables operate between telephone terminal stations. Long submarine cables have similar limitations to long telephone lines and before valve amplifiers were available their channel capacity was very limited and the signals, usually simple low frequency tones, suffered severe attenuation. Valve repeaters which can be built into the cable and submerged have changed this completely. The first transatlantic telephone cable was laid in 1956 and provided 36 telephone circuits at a cost per circuit of about £150 a mile. Cable making is one of the few fields in telecommunications in which the British have maintained their lead over the Americans and research by the G.P.O. and firms such as Submarine Cable and Standard Telephones and Cables resulted in big improvements in cable links. Dr Brockbank of the G.P.O. invented a new light-weight cable with improved performance, replacing the heavy armoured cable which is now used in shallow waters only. The G.P.O. also developed deep sea repeaters, using transistors and miniaturized components, which could withstand pressures of up to 5 tons per square inch and operate satisfactorily without maintenance for twenty years. The new techniques were used in the Oban to Newfoundland cable link, first in the chain between Britain and Australia, which was laid in 1961. This provides 80 circuits at a cost of about £45 a mile per circuit. The latest cable, TAT-3, laid by the Americans in 1963 across the North Atlantic, provided 128 circuits at a cost of about £20 per mile and they are thinking of a system to be laid in 1967 which will provide 720 circuits. Not to be outdone, the G.P.O. has plans for a 1,000-circuit cable which will reduce the cost per circuit to under £5 per mile and have sufficient channel capacity to transmit live television programmes without serious loss of quality. Other ingenious electronic techniques in the transmission and reception of signals have also led to increased economy and efficiency in cable performance. One of the latest of these, the American-designed T.A.S.I. (Time Assignment Speech Interpolation), interleaves one conversation into the gaps and pauses of another, so doubling the cable capacity.

The present submarine telephone cable systems have reached a stage in development where they are competitive with the communications satellites so far designed. Inter-continental communication has increased enormously since 1956 when the first transatlantic telephone cable was completed. Before that, calls from Britain were under 3,000 per week; soon after the cable was opened they increased to over 6,000 per week; they are now approaching 20,000 per week. The permanent lines leased to Governments and military users include the 'hot line' which links the White House with the Kremlin, and which played such a critical part in the Cuban crisis of 1962. The volume of telegraph and TELEX (a G.P.O. teleprinter facility) traffic which flows along the transatlantic and transpacific cables is also increasing steadily. One very significant type of traffic which is now building up on the new lines is transmission of data from the computers of business organizations, and this may soon transform the cable channels into the elements of a network linking the computers of different continents which will affect profoundly the future of international relations.

Today there are over 150 million telephones in the world and the number is increasing at the rate of 10 million a year. The customs and daily life of hundreds of millions of people have been changed by the existence of a telephone network on this huge scale – a network which depends on the increasing use of electronic devices and electronic techniques. At the last meeting of the International Telecommunications Union, which took place in Rome at the end of 1963, a world-wide direct dialling system was initiated. Dialling codes were agreed on to be used in the next forty years on a global telephone system with an anticipated 600 million subscribers. There is nothing fanciful about these plans; the I.T.U. is one of the few truly international organizations which has survived the hot and cold wars of our times and it functions very efficiently. The first step was taken in 1964 when a large part of Europe was linked up in the direct dialling system and subscribers on S.T.D. (Subscriber Trunk Dialling) in most of the important West European towns can now dial one another directly. Operators in London dial numbers in the United States and, since the opening of the transpacific cable COMPAC, numbers in Australia, directly.

The increase in complexity and size of the telephone systems and the increasing range of services which they offer make it essential for all switching operations to be carried out speedily and with the utmost reliability. Electronic switching is more than 1,000 times faster than the electro-mechanical switches and selector mechanisms of existing automatic exchanges which they are beginning to replace. In Britain the G.P.O. has been planning the change over to electronic exchanges for some time and in America the changeover has already started, although it is expected to take about thirty-five years to convert all the telephones in the United States.

The shape of the telephone service to come can be forecast by the facilities offered to some 200 subscribers on the world's first permanent electronic central office at Succasunna, sixty miles south-west of New York, which was opened in 1965. Housewives can order their groceries simply by dialling the supermarket's computer, or, if they prefer to touch and smell the food which they buy, they can turn on the oven in the kitchen at home while they are out shopping by dialling their own numbers plus a simple code. Office workers who get an engaged signal will be notified by the ringing of their own instruments when the desired line becomes free. Subscribers who intend to be away from their own telephones for some time can dial a code number plus the number of a line where they can be reached and all incoming calls will be transferred there automatically until further instructions are dialled. The systems engineers of the Bell Telephone Laboratories in New York, where the new system was developed, say that it is so flexible that many other services will be possible in the near future. Electronic switching will have as revolutionary an effect on the telephone as automatic switching has had.

## MOBILE RADIO AND FREQUENCY MODULATION

The progress in line communications due to electronics has been brought about largely without the knowledge of the layman, but mobile communications have always intrigued the general public and the role played in these by radio and electronics is much better known. The 'walkie-talkie' – a small battery-powered radio transmitter and receiver which can be strapped to a man's back – was developed during the Second World War for short range communication between soldiers under battle conditions. Larger versions were fitted into tanks, army trucks and similar vehicles. After the war improved equipment was developed for police cars, ambulances, taxis, fire-brigade tenders, doctors' and press reporters' cars, vessels such as tugs and fire-fighting launches in ports, and so on. In large-scale engineering works operations can be directed and coordinated from a central point by fitting mobile radio-telephones to bulldozers and cranes.

In general such systems are simplified by being tuned permanently to selected wavelengths which are allocated by the official communications control body in the country concerned. In a typical system, such as that used for police cars or taxi-call services, headquarters is connected to a number of strategically situated automatic stations which are unattended but supplied each with its own aerial, so that cars are always within range of the headquarters' transmission.

One of the main drawbacks of mobile radio communication, the difficulty of eliminating static and man-made noise and of maintaining precisely the right transmitting and receiving frequencies, was overcome by the use of frequency modulation. F.M. was invented in the thirties by the American university professor Edwin Armstrong, who found himself involved in a struggle with the large American broadcasting networks which were then committed to amplitude modulation. The difference between the two methods can be appreciated by comparing the radio transmitter to a pump. In amplitude modulation this electrical pump pushes and pulls the carrier current into and out of the aerial many thousands of times in a second, while the current is modulated by a voice current from a microphone which increases or decreases the strength or amplitude of the carrier in sympathy with the voice fluctuations. Note that in A.M. the pump operates throughout at constant speed. In frequency modulation the amplitude of the aerial current remains constant but the *speed* of the pump is varied according to the fluctuations in the voice current. In the receiver, the F.M. waves are combined with the waves from a local oscillator to produce intermediate frequency waves – the usual heterodyne system – and then pass to a 'limiter'. This is a valve circuit which lops off the tops and bottoms of the waves so that they all emerge with the same amplitude. They then pass to a final detector which converts their differences in frequency back into sounds. Since static and most other forms of interference are amplitude modulated they are virtually eliminated in the receiver.

The prolonged battle waged by the American vested interests against Armstrong finally drove him to suicide in 1954, but the advantages of F.M. were too great to be ignored and the American networks have now been largely converted to it. Although F.M.

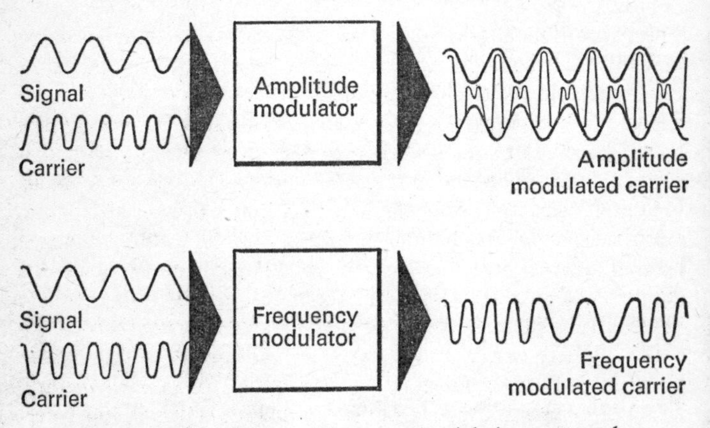


*Figure 35.* Amplitude and frequency modulation compared.

requires more bandwidth than A.M. it is possible to operate several F.M. stations at the same frequency with very little mutual interference so that many more stations can be placed in the same region. The British public has become familiar with the high quality and noise-free reception obtainable with F.M. since the B.B.C.'s V.H.F. transmissions using F.M. have been in service. F.M. is replacing A.M. to an increasing extent for radio broadcasting from fixed transmitters as the available frequency spectrum becomes more and more crowded, and has replaced it almost entirely for mobile systems.

The use of the thin film and integrated circuit techniques described in Chapter 3 for mobile radio systems may lead to very interesting developments in the near future. The trend is illustrated by a recent transmitter-receiver developed in Canada which will operate on any one of 3,500 channels although it weighs less than 10 lb. and measures $6 \times 4 \times 1\frac{1}{2}$ inches so that it can easily be held in the hand. With the extended use of microelectronics we may expect to see completely self-contained pocket radio-telephones available not only to the police and similar bodies but to private individuals as well.

## MASERS AND LASERS

The revolution in communications which we have reviewed so far can be attributed to the application of electronics, including the miniaturization of electronic components, to the established technologies of the telegraph, telephone and radio. An entirely new development in electronics now offers the possibility of further revolutionary advances in communications (and in other fields too) and these are now receiving attention from physicists and electronic engineers. I refer to masers, which include lasers, a class of devices which has been very much in the limelight recently. A few words about 'noise' and the use of microwaves will help those unfamiliar with the technical background to appreciate the value of these devices.

In the widest sense, noise in any system of communication arises from any of the many different processes which may interfere with the system and which are not under the control of the operators of the system. The word 'noise' has a precise significance in the sense in which it is used here and should not be confused with the popular sense which involves pleasant and unpleasant sensations. The sweetest music is 'noise' if it drowns the conversation of two people who wish to exchange information about, say, fat-stock prices. One of the important criteria of any communication channel is obtained by comparing the amount of energy in the intelligence conveyed at any instant to the amount of energy represented by the total noise transmitted: the so-called signal-to-noise ratio. A large part of the technical effort in communications is expended in the attempts to improve the signal-to-noise ratio. There are many sources of noise, both man-made and natural, with which we are unfortunately only too familiar, but there is one source of noise which is a limiting factor in telecommunications and cannot be eliminated in the ordinary way. This is the noise due to the random motions of electrons in a conductor which increases as the temperature increases and disappears only at the absolute zero of temperature, —273 °C. All ordinary amplifiers generate this noise at temperatures above absolute zero, and the noise factor of an amplifier may be expressed in terms of 'noise temperature', or the absolute temperature of any object which, when emitting heat radiation into the amplifier, doubles its noise output. It is clear that no signal whose level is below the level of inherent thermal noise of an amplifier can be distinguished at the output of the amplifier. This was the inexorable limiting factor in all attempts to detect, for example, radar echoes from distant targets, or the very weak signals from remote radio stars – until the invention of the maser.

The kind of amplification considered so far depends on the controlled release of stored energy, such as the energy of a storage battery, by the action of electrons flowing through a vacuum, a gas or a semiconductor. In a maser, energy is stored by pumping it into individual molecules and atoms and released by allowing these excited molecules and atoms to react with electromagnetic waves of exactly the right frequency. Hence the name maser: 'Microwave Amplification by Stimulated Emission of Radiation'.

This interaction between atoms and radiation is really quite familiar since light from the sun or from a lamp is due to the spontaneous emission of radiation from atoms in which electrons are jumping from higher to lower energy levels. Similarly, absorption of electromagnetic waves of the right frequency by atoms with high energy electrons will result in such electrons dropping to lower energy states, with release of quanta of energy which may be absorbed by the stimulating wave. This amounts to amplification of the electromagnetic waves, which is not affected by the random motions of electrons. While the noise temperature of a good amplifier of the conventional type in the microwave region lies between 1,000 and 2,000°K, that of a maser amplifier is less than 2°K, which represents hardly any amplifier noise at all. This means that the minimum amount of microwave energy which can be detected by a maser amplifier is about 10 photons, or about

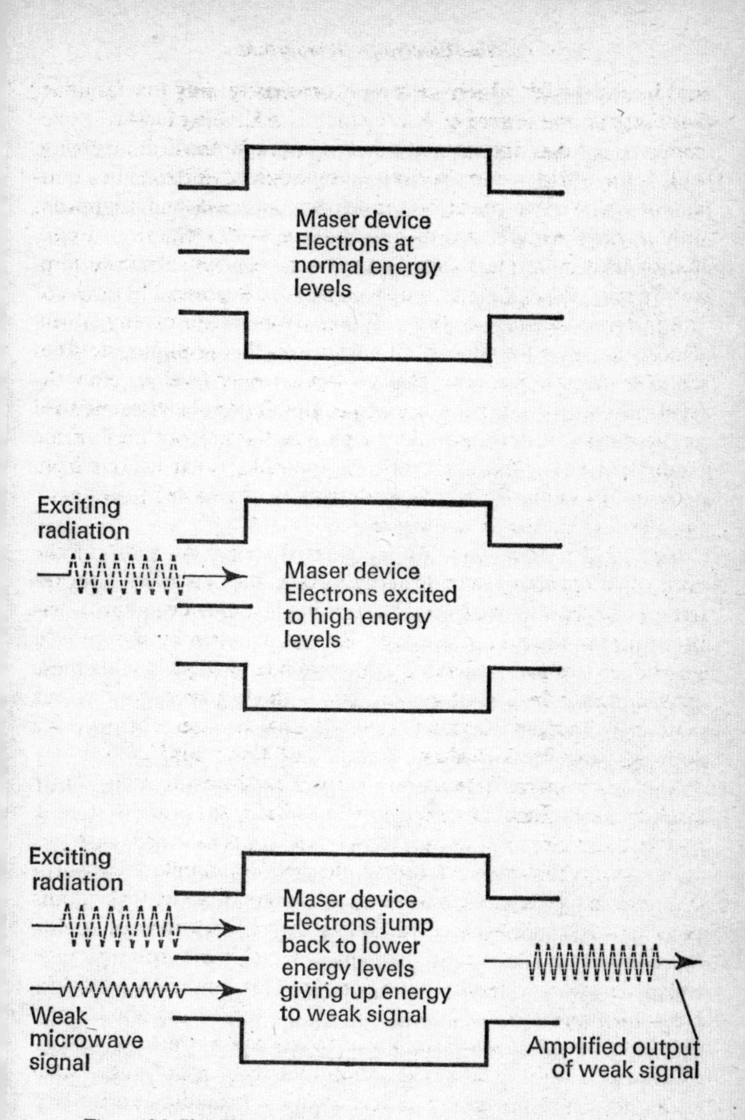


*Figure 36.* Simplified diagram to show the principle of a maser.

a thousand times less than the minimum detectable with a good conventional amplifier.

The development of radar and wartime communication systems led to a greatly extended use of microwaves and understanding of their properties. By 1945 the shortest microwaves which had been used were about 0·5 centimetres long corresponding to a frequency of about 60 Gigacycles/second (1 Gigacycle = 1,000 million cycles). Scientists and engineers became very interested in the possibilities of shorter wavelengths extending into the millimetre and 'sub-millimetre' regions of the electromagnetic spectrum. The desire to experiment with these very short high frequency waves extending into the infra-red and even into the visible spectrum was not due simply to a thirst for knowledge but was also motivated by the pressing need for more bits of the electromagnetic spectrum to accommodate communication channels which could not be fitted into the overcrowded frequency bands lower down in the spectrum. It is not hard to see why there is more room at the top in the e.m. spectrum. If we allow a frequency bandwidth of 10,000 cycles for one communication channel, the part of the e.m. spectrum bounded by frequencies of 1 million cycles/second and 2 million cycles/second (i.e. a considerable part of the medium wave radio broadcast band) can accommodate a maximum of 100 such channels without overlapping, whereas a region in the sub-millimetre waves bounded by 1 million million cycles/second and 2 million million cycles/second could accommodate a theoretical maximum of no less than 100 million of such channels. It is true that the closer we approach the visible spectrum the more the waves resemble light waves and since such waves do not penetrate material obstacles in their path, they are suitable only for line of sight communication; but this is not a drawback in the case of, for example, communication satellites.

Intensive research into the production of millimetre and sub-millimetre waves, which started in about 1950, soon bore fruit. The idea of using stimulated emission of radiation for amplification of very short waves came independently from three teams of physicists in 1951. These were: a group at Columbia University led by C. H. Townes, who holds the fundamental patents on the maser; A. Prokhorov and N. Basov of the Lebedev Institute in Moscow; and J. Weber at the University of Maryland. The

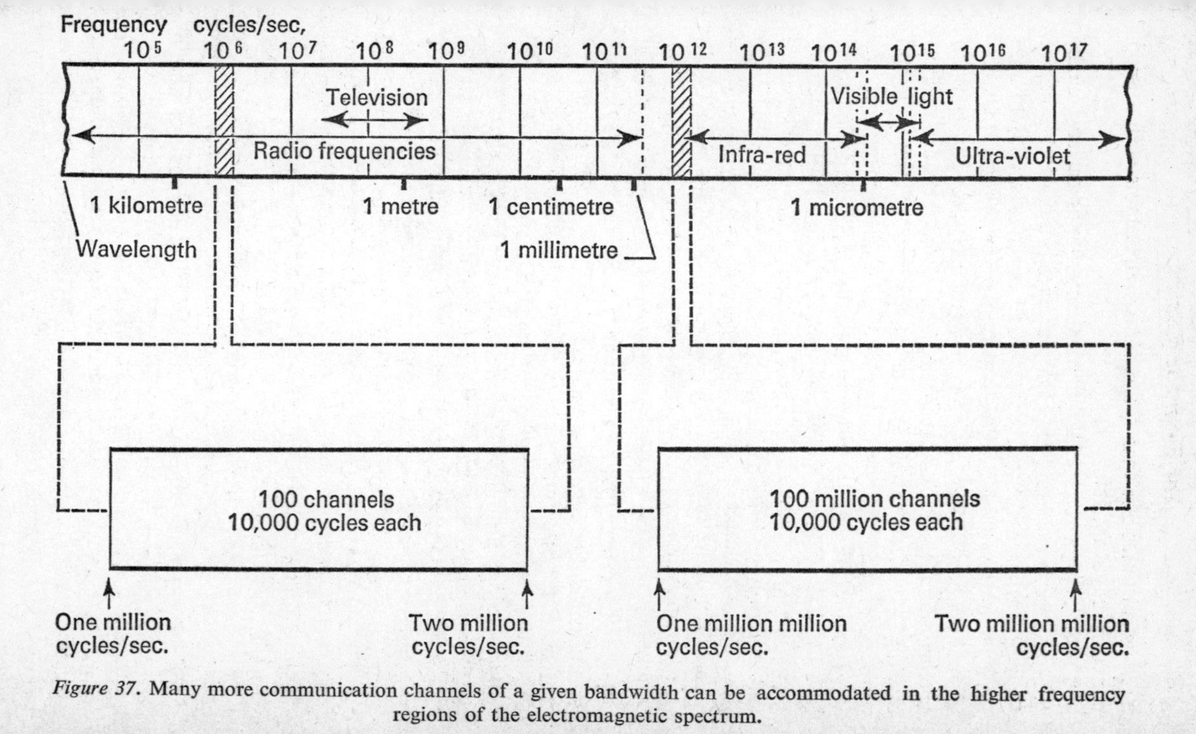


*Figure 37.* Many more communication channels of a given bandwidth can be accommodated in the higher frequency regions of the electromagnetic spectrum.

original ammonia-beam maser makes use of a beam of molecules of ammonia gas which are shot through a small hole into an evacuated cavity. Here the molecules are subjected to electric fields which push and pull them in such a way that the molecules in an excited state are concentrated and focused through a hole into another cavity designed so that they can resonate with the microwaves there and give up their extra energy to them. In 1953, J. P. Gordon, a young graduate at Columbia, succeeded in making a maser which oscillated and could therefore generate the very high frequency waves as well as amplify them.

Masers have made revolutionary advances possible in a number of different fields. They are up to 1,000 times more sensitive as amplifiers of microwaves than any other type of amplifier and introduce practically no noise; this has permitted a great extension in the range of radar and long-distance communication. Lincoln Laboratory has operated a transcontinental communication link via the moon, using maser amplifiers. Maser amplifiers mounted on radio telescopes can increase even their great range by a factor of 10, allowing us to reach out to the bounds of the known universe. Maser oscillators generate frequencies many thousands of times higher than can be obtained with any electronic tube and they have opened up the regions of the electromagnetic spectrum beyond microwaves for exploitation by electronic techniques. Because of the very constant frequency with which masers can be made to oscillate they can be used as master controls for atomic clocks of unbelievable accuracy: an error not exceeding 1 second in 10,000 years has already been achieved. Even more exciting possibilities can be added to this list by the inclusion of masers which operate in the infra-red and optical regions of the spectrum where they have come to be widely known as lasers.

The laser – Light Amplification by Stimulated Emission of Radiation – was a natural development from the maser and many researchers in different countries have contributed in the last decade to the design and applications of various types of laser. The first maser to achieve successful operation at optical frequencies was built in the U.S.A. in 1960 by T. H. Maiman of the Hughes Research and Development Laboratory. He used a pink ruby with plane parallel faces, encircled by a tube which produced flashes of extremely bright blue light. Ruby is a hard crystal of

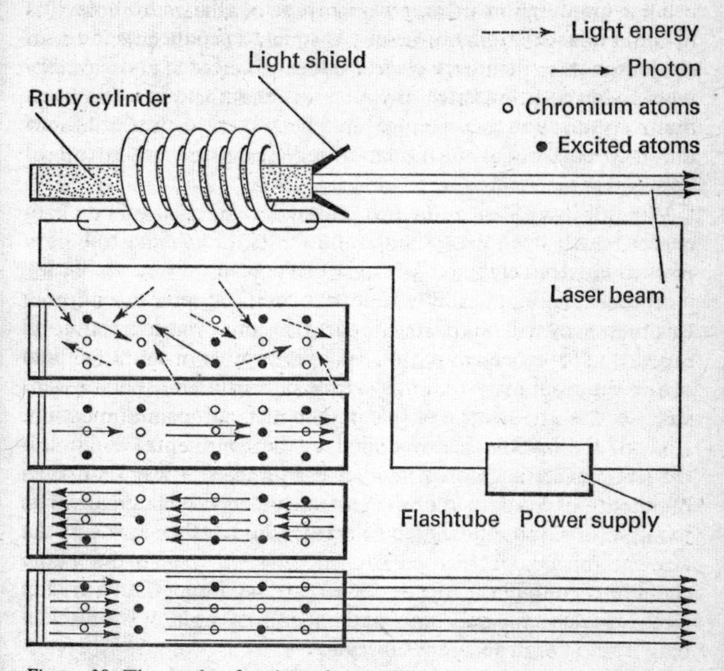


*Figure 38.* The mode of action of the ruby laser; chromium atoms in the ruby cylinder are excited to higher energy levels by light from the helical flash tube. One end of the ruby cylinder is totally silvered and the other 99 per cent silvered. After repeated reflections between the ends of the crystal the energy released by the excited atoms emerges through the partially silvered end as an intense beam of pure infra-red light.

aluminium oxide and the red colour is due to a small proportion of chromium atoms, which can be excited by light of the right wavelength. In the original laser the excited chromium atoms were kicked into energy levels where maser action (see above) could take place. The energy of the excited atoms was transferred to infra-red radiation which, after repeated reflection between the parallel faces of the crystal, was emitted as an intermittent but very intense beam of pure infra-red light.

The first laser was followed up very quickly by Javan, Bennett and Herriott of the Bell Telephone Laboratories with a laser using a discharge in helium gas to transfer energy from excited helium atoms to atoms of neon gas so as to produce continuous oscillation at optical frequencies. Intensive research and development followed in America, Britain and Russia and in a few years many crystals and gas mixtures had been used to produce lasers and they emerged from the laboratory stage and began to find applications.

Why all this effort on lasers? These devices have unique properties which open up some dazzling vistas. First, the radiation emitted is extremely pure. The light of the laser may be oscillating a thousand, million, million times a second but the fluctuation in this frequency will not be much more than one cycle in a thousand seconds! No other source of radiation, either natural or man made, can even approach this degree of purity and stability. We shall see the importance of this in communications in a moment.

Next, the laser is highly directive; the beam spreads far less than any other source of parallel light known – less than one-hundredth of the spread of the best searchlight. It is thus the best 'straight line' now available to science and technology. As an illustration, a laser focused by a good telescope on the moon could be used to illuminate a spot on earth no larger than a cricket pitch. This extreme coherence and linearity of the laser has already been put to use in accurate surveying.

Finally, the intensity of radiation in a laser beam is much greater than that of any other known radiant source. The power used to generate the beam, which can be relatively small, can be focused in the beam to a density equal to a hundred million times the original. The needle of light from the laser can therefore concentrate enormous energy in a very small area. It will, for instance, quickly drill a very fine hole through a block of steel, and evaporate refractory materials in its path. Lasers are now being produced for applications requiring great precision such as eye surgery, accurate measurement, fine control of machines, exact machining of very hard materials, and so on, but our particular interest in this chapter is their application to the art of communications.

The extraordinary frequency purity of laser beams makes it possible for optical frequencies to be used as exactly defined carrier frequencies for communication channels. The practical engineering problems of finding suitable means to modulate the beams at the transmitter and demodulate them at the receiver are already being solved. The great prize to be won is the huge increase in the available channel capacity. The insuperable difficulty of finding enough bandwidth at ordinary radio or microwave frequencies disappears at optical frequencies. The entire bandwidth used so far for radio and microwaves is equivalent to not more than one thousandth of the optical range. The optical part of the electromagnetic spectrum, extending over more than three thousand million megacycles, could provide an individual communication channel for everyone on earth. Such channels were not engineering propositions before lasers, but the very precise location of frequencies which these devices make possible, and the great directivity of their beams, make it technically possible to have these millions of adjacent channels with optical range and without mutual interference. Haldane's imaginative forecast quoted at the head of this chapter no longer seems so far away.

The ability of laser beams to cross vast distances and pinpoint remote targets justifies a little speculation about possible future developments. Using large 200-inch telescopes outside the earth's atmosphere to direct laser beams they should be visible to the naked eye at distances of the order of one-tenth of a light year. With another telescope to aid the eye a beam dispatched in this way could be detected at something like 100 light years' distance. This may be the basis of inter-planetary communication in the future and of inter-stellar communication in the remote future.

### COMMUNICATION BY SATELLITE

The most spectacular aspect of the revolution in communications is the use of artificial satellites. This may be considered as a logical extension of the system of microwave relays with the aerials placed many hundreds of miles above the earth to give a long line of sight path. To the reader who has become accustomed to the exploits of the space age there might seem nothing very extraordinary in the idea of a telephone conversation with a friend across the Atlantic which is bounced off a ball circling hundreds of miles above the earth, or of watching a television programme which has been re-radiated from an electronic package inside such a ball, but to the average pre-1950 telecommunication engineer such a scheme would have been regarded as pure fantasy. However, there was at least one prophet before 1950.

The idea of using satellites as relays for communication was first put forward by Arthur C. Clarke, the well-known writer of science fiction and one of the founders of the British Interplanetary Society, in an article which appeared in the October 1945 issue of the *Wireless World.* Not the least remarkable thing about this article was that the system proposed by Clarke consisted of three 'synchronous' satellites which would give complete round-the-world coverage. Of the many possible systems which could be used it now seems likely that the one suggested by Clarke will be adopted, but the successful execution of the idea had to wait for twenty years since it demands the accumulated experience and the latest advances in the space, communications and electronics arts. Neither the commercial incentives nor the economic justification for satellite relays existed until the demand which was stimulated by the transatlantic telephone cable of 1951, and the subsequent cables, grew faster than the capacity of these links to handle the large number of conversations, the masses of data, and the television programmes and pictures which they might be required to carry.

The very large resources required to initiate and carry through an experimental programme leading to an efficient satellite communications system were provided by the U.S. Government, through its National Aeronautics and Space Administration, and by powerful American Corporations such as the American Telephone and Telegraph and the Hughes Aircraft Company, but the technologies drawn on were based on the contributions of scientists and engineers from many countries, and the successful completion of a world communication system will depend on international cooperation.

The first demonstration that satellite communication was a practical possibility was provided in December 1958 when SCORE, a radio receiver and transmitter, was put into orbit by an Atlas missile long enough to send a Christmas message from President Eisenhower round the world. In August 1960, ECHO, a self-inflating balloon with an aluminized envelope, was used as a passive reflector for powerful radio beams carrying high-quality telephone circuits across the Atlantic, but the experiments ceased when the balloon became deformed. An active repeater satellite called COURIER which carried a receiver-recorder transmitter, was launched successfully in October 1960 but ceased to function after only 18 days. The first attempt by the Americans to realize their *West Ford* project – the dispersion of millions of fine copper needles to form a permanent belt in orbit round the earth and act as a reflector for microwaves – was made in October 1961, but proved abortive as the needles failed to disperse. The project was sharply criticized by astronomers who considered that it might interfere with astronomical observations, but the Americans may have wanted it as a war-time system which no enemy could sweep from the sky. In any case it would have formed a very limited communication system since it was purely passive and would require very large amounts of power to be radiated from the ground stations to get detectable reflections.

In 1962 came the active repeater communications satellites RELAY and TELSTAR. RELAY was an official civilian project of N.A.S.A. designed to have a capacity of about 100 voice channels and one television channel. It was TELSTAR which really put satellite communications 'on the map' for the people of Britain and Europe, and I think it worth describing in some detail. TELSTAR was designed and built by the Bell Telephone Laboratories to obtain information on the performance of an active satellite capable of transmitting broad-band signals and also to obtain data about the space environment and its effect on the electronic devices in the satellite. This information would be sent back by a complex telemetry system with 115 channels to the ground tracking stations, which could also be equipped to operate a command system in the satellite. TELSTAR is a rough sphere, about 35 ins. in diameter and weighs about 170 lb. Inside is a 20-inch diameter canister held by nylon cords and containing all the electronic equipment set in plastic foam. There are over 1,000 transistors, 1,500 diodes, one valve and a travelling-wave tube. F.M. signals centred at frequencies close to 6,000 megacycles/second can be received, amplified about 5,000 million times, and re-radiated with a power of about 2 watts at frequencies near 4,000 mc/s. In addition, a low-power beacon signal can be transmitted on 4,080 mc/s for tracking, and command and telemetry signals can be sent and received at 123 and 136 mc/s respectively.

The electronic equipment is powered by 3,600 silicon solar cells, arranged round the sphere, which charge a nickel-cadmium storage battery, but when all the equipment is switched on it consumes power faster than the solar cells can produce it so that provision is made to turn the communication equipment on and off by command from the ground.

Telstar was launched by the N.A.S.A. from Cape Canaveral (now Cape Kennedy) on 10 July 1962, in a three-stage rocket. It went into an elliptical orbit with perigee 600 miles, apogee 3,500 miles, period 160 mins. and inclination of orbital plane to equator 45 degrees. These figures are very close to the design objectives and the subsequent track of the satellite was substantially what had been predicted. It traces different paths on the surface of the earth with each successive orbit, and the period of mutual visibility between American and British ground stations started with periods of about 30 minutes occurring three or four times every 24 hours, but this period decreased steadily. Three ground stations took part in the Telstar experiment: in the U.S.A. at Andover, Maine; in Britain at Goonhilly Downs, Cornwall; and in France at Pleumeur Bodou, Brittany. The American and French stations were designed by Bell Telephone Laboratories and each have a horn aerial 177 ft long, with aperture 60 ft square, and weighing 370 tons. The aerials run on circular rail tracks for adjustment of azimuth and can be tilted for elevation adjustment. The Goonhilly station, designed and built in Britain, is situated on the Lizard in Cornwall less than four miles from the site at Poldhu from which Marconi sent his historic transatlantic signal in 1901.

The Goonhilly aerial is a remarkable example of modern engineering. It is a parabolic dish, 85 ft in diameter, weighing about 870 tons, which rotates on a turntable for changes in azimuth and on horizontal bearings for changes in elevation. This massive structure, designed to operate in wind velocities up to 65 m.p.h., was provided with powerful servo-controlled driving motors to track the moving satellite automatically within a few minutes of arc. The data for the automatic steering is processed in a computer. Since the signal received from the satellite is less than a million-millionth of a watt an essential part of the electronic equipment is a maser mounted close behind the dish.

After a false start, due to a misunderstanding between American and British teams, the G.P.O. engineers at Goonhilly acquired the signals from the satellite as it rose over the horizon on the night of 11–12 July and excellent television pictures from Andover were obtained. That night the first live television transmission between Europe and America was made from Goonhilly to Andover and millions of viewers in America, Britain and France were able to share the triumph of the engineers and scientists who had worked on the project. On the following day the first two-way transatlantic telephony tests were made using 12 telephone channels in each direction, and very good quality, low-noise, telephone circuits were achieved. Subsequent tests showed that at least 600 good-quality telephone circuits could be obtained by satellite. On 16 July the first colour television signals to be sent by satellite were transmitted from Goonhilly to Telstar and received back at Goonhilly with very little loss in quality after the satellite had travelled 10,000 miles in space. Experiments continued with Telstar and one in conjunction with Relay is particularly interesting. In November 1963 a two-way transatlantic link was established between meetings of doctors in Chicago and London. In the morning a panel of experts in Chicago answered questions from British doctors via Telstar and in the afternoon a British panel answered questions from Chicago via Relay. Telstar is expected to remain in orbit for about 200 years but the electronic equipment has been switched off.

The possibilities of satellite communication were placed beyond doubt by Telstar and Relay, but neither represented economic operational systems because their relatively low altitude cut their mutual visibility, and consequently useful operating time, to less than 2 hours in 24. Various types of orbits have been considered, circular and elliptical, in equatorial and polar planes, at heights ranging from 1,000 to 12,000 miles, and so on. The special case of a satellite orbiting in the equatorial plane of the earth in the direction of rotation of the earth and at a height of 22,300 miles offers many advantages. Such a satellite appears stationary from the earth and three such satellites would be adequate for world-wide cover without a break.

The Communications Satellite Corporation was formed in the United States and, in conjunction with N.A.S.A., took over the Syncom programme to test the performance of synchronous satellites. Syncom 2 was successfully launched into a synchronous orbit in July 1963 and in the next twelve months demonstrated very convincingly the advantages of the synchronous system. The drum-shaped satellite was fitted, in addition to the most sophisticated electronic equipment for transmission, reception, telemetry, command, power supplies and sun sensing, with gas-jets which made it the first controllable communications satellite. It went to its predicted position over Africa and was then manoeuvred to a longitude of 55 degrees west over South America; the control precision proved to be accurate to within a hundredth of a degree. The aerial beam of the spinning satellite was directed at the earth to within two degrees by rotating it gently four days after launch. It obeyed faithfully all the commands of the ground stations and in March 1964 was moved westward at about 1½ degrees a day so that it was available for communications in the Pacific Ocean area in May of that year. By March 1964 it had logged more than 2,000 hours of communications, including voice, television, teletype, facsimile and data transmission, and had responded to 12,000 commands switching the electronic equipment and gas-jets on and off without a single failure. One of the problems which had given rise to doubt about synchronous systems was the time taken for a signal to go and return the great distance of the satellite, since even at the speed of light this is about 0·3 seconds, but the delay did not prove troublesome in normal conversations. The Olympic Games of 1964 provided an opportunity for a world-wide demonstration of the Syncom system, when Syncom 3 was launched on 19 August and steered into position over the international date line and on 1 October began to transmit excellent television pictures of the Games in Tokyo to the West Coast of the United States. From there the pictures were fed into the American microwave network to Buffalo and then via the Canadian network to Montreal, where the pictures were recorded on magnetic tape and flown to Hamburg by jet plane to link up with the Eurovision network.

1965 was the year of decision for the Communications Satellite Corporation (COMSAT). It decided to go ahead with the synchronous system developed by the Hughes Aircraft Company in preference to the Bell-R.C.A. system of medium altitude satellites about 6,000 miles out. The first will need three (or possibly three

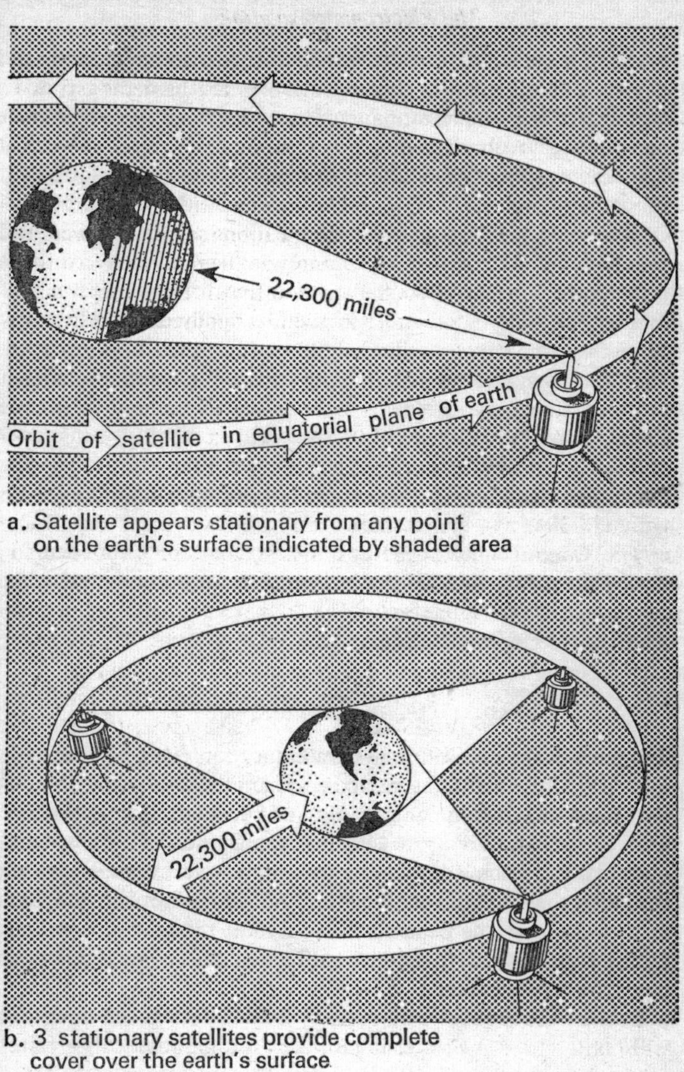


*Figure 39.* One synchronous satellite can provide direct communication with more than one-third of the earth's surface; three such satellites suitably positioned can provide total cover.

pairs) of the satellites and the second 24 if they are in uncontrolled orbits or 12 if they are in controlled orbits. Hughes's experts claim that the cost of building, launching and testing the satellites is roughly proportional to the number of satellites required to meet a specified performance and they quote a figure of a little over £1 million per satellite. The synchronous satellites, however, must be very accurately controlled and maintained in altitude and precisely on station for the maximum use of their available power, which needs to be greater than that for the much nearer medium-altitude satellites. The issue was finally decided by Early Bird, a synchronous satellite which was launched in April 1965. This was designed to handle 240 two-way telephone channels between Europe and North America and, acts as a telephone exchange poised in the sky. It has a more powerful transmitter and the aerial was designed with a narrower beam than the earlier Syncoms. The Hughes Company are preparing to follow it up with HS-304, a 4-feet diameter drum with a solar array generating twice as much power as Early Bird and some very cunning devices to ensure that the power is used to the best advantage for communications. Three or six HS-304s would constitute a complete global communication system.

## SOME FUTURE DEVELOPMENTS

The pace of the revolution in communications, as I have tried to indicate in this chapter, seems to be accelerating. A rapidly expanding world network of cable, radio and satellite links now carries an even more rapidly increasing message traffic. As the new communication systems are brought into service to satisfy rising demands they create new facilities and new relationships which in turn increase the demands. This makes the near future both exciting and difficult to predict, but I will hazard some predictions based on present trends.

In the next twenty years most technically advanced countries will build national electronic networks for communications, just as they have built networks for the supply of electric power. These electronic grids will be capable of dealing with a very wide band of very high frequencies and will consist of line-of-sight microwave relay links, waveguides, pipes and cables between the main centres of population, and branching like the electricity grid or telephone networks to individual users within those centres. Eventually the telephone network will become part of the communication grid. Electronic techniques such as magnetic storage band compression, and pulse code modulation, will make the most economic use of the grid possible. The grid will carry national and local television and radio programmes and every kind of visual and non-visual information exchange between government and official bodies, industrial, business, scientific, educational, health and recreation organizations and private individuals. When the grids are well established they will be used by the postal services for electronic transmission of letters by teleprinter and facsimile with suitable privacy circuits. Television, facsimile and electronic recording and reproduction will eventually replace most of the existing methods of printing and distributing words and pictures and by the end of the century I think newspapers and books will be dealt with mainly on the grid.

Within the next twenty years also a process of integration of the national telephone networks and the national communication grids into a world communication network will develop. It will depend on submarine cable, radio and satellite links and the extensive use of microelectronics will allow sufficient redundancy – the provision of much more capacity for any job than is normally necessary so that total failure is very unlikely – to ensure complete reliability of such links. Through the world network will flow the world-wide television programmes; international news and propaganda; the conversations of any of some 300 million telephone subscribers, a large proportion of whom will be able to dial one another directly and cheaply; weather information; aircraft to ground and ship to shore communications; industrial and business data from plants and companies thousands of miles apart. Hot lines between the world's governments will provide colour television as well as speech circuits so that not a blush will escape the eyes of the top persons.

The effects of these networks on society will obviously be very great and some of them will be discussed in later chapters but I think that I have ventured enough prediction for this chapter. Readers are invited to try a few predictions on the subject themselves; the possibilities are endless.

# 5

# The Universal Eye

One picture is worth a thousand words.
*Old Chinese Proverb*

FOR many people television is simply a modern form of entertainment to be enjoyed at home with no more effort than the turn of a switch, or avoided if the programmes are not to one's liking. But in reality it is much more than that. It is an invention of greater scope and significance than the invention of movable type and it is probable that, together with other electron-optical techniques, it will largely supplant the use of movable type before the end of the century. The part played by television in the electronic revolution has already been touched on in the chapter on communications and will be referred to in later chapters, but at least one whole chapter of this book is required to do justice to this subject.

## PICTURES BY WIRE

The introduction of wire telegraphy in the mid-nineteenth century set a number of inventors thinking about sending pictures by wire. The first crude system of photo-telegraphy on record was invented in 1862 by a certain Abbé Caselli, whose experiments were encouraged by Napoleon III. Caselli devised a method of converting portions of a photograph (daguerreotypes were all the rage at the time) into electric signals which were sent along telegraph wires and reconstructed at the other end. He opened a number of commercial stations in France between which messages in the sender's own handwriting could be sent and received, but the process was painfully slow and had more novelty than practical value.

The selenium photocell was invented in 1873 and this provided a suitable means of converting the light and shade of an image into electric currents, but, rather surprisingly, the transmission of moving pictures by wire was achieved before the first really practical transmission of still pictures by the Frenchman, Belin, in 1904. This original form of television was due to a mechanical invention: the scanning disc, invented by Paul Nipkow in 1884. The scanning process, common to both still and moving pictures, is based on persistence of vision in the human eye. The eye does not notice interruptions of vision which last less than about one twentieth of a second, and any sequence of pictures presented to the eye at a rate of more than 20 per second appears as a moving picture. Nipkow's disc was perforated with a series of small holes in a single spiral, each slightly nearer to the centre than the one preceding it. The disc was placed between a source of light and the object to be illuminated and rotated so that the light shone through one hole after the other, and in one complete turn every element of the object had been illuminated in a definite order. After reflection from the object the light spot was directed to a selenium cell so that the light and shade of the object was converted into a varying current. Nipkow's attempts to convert the electrical currents back into images with a synchronized disc were never quite successful and his was only the first of a number of mechanical systems for television which did not get beyond the experimental stage.

In 1889, Professor L. Weiller replaced the Nipkow disc by a revolving drum fitted with a number of small mirrors which reflected the image into a selenium screen. In 1907, Professor Boris Rosing of the St Petersburg Technological Institute used mirror drums in combination with a Braun tube (see p. 66) into which he had inserted a screen of photoelectric cells, and succeeded in getting some very faint images. Vladimir Zworykin was one of Rosing's pupils.

## ELECTRONIC TELEVISION

Although it was possible to transmit and receive crude images with mechanical scanning this was to prove unsatisfactory for television. For sufficient detail to be recognizable, some 100,000 elements of a moving image have to be sent more than 20 times a second and mechanical systems do not operate satisfactorily or synchronize accurately at such speeds. It was suggested as early as 1908 by the British experimenter A. A. Campbell-Swinton that

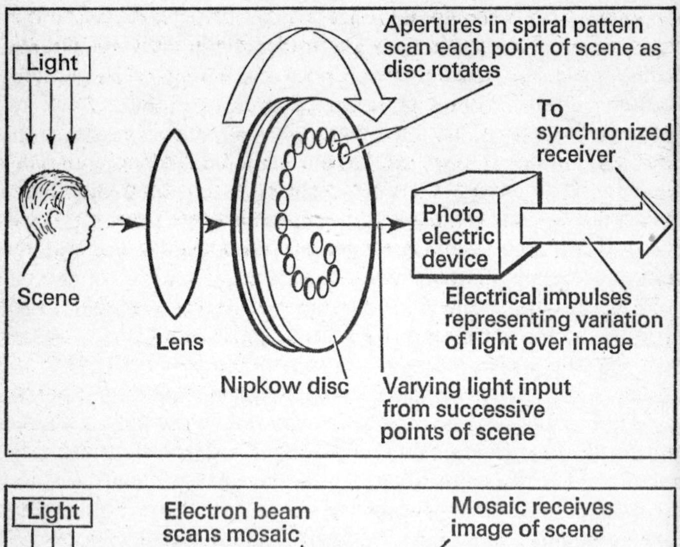


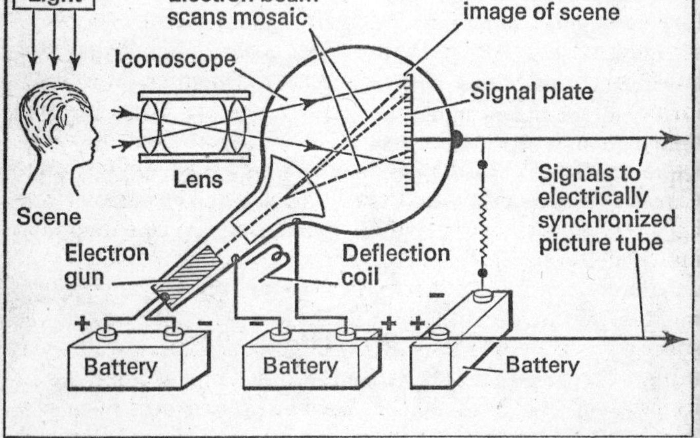


*Figure 40.* Mechanical and electronic scanning systems compared (see page 131).

electronic tubes be used for scanning, but this idea did not bear fruit until twenty years later when Zworykin invented the iconoscope (see p. 69). Meanwhile mechanical systems of great ingenuity were perfected in America by H. E. Ives of the Bell Telephone Laboratories, and in Britain by J. L. Baird. The first public demonstration of mechanical television was given in 1925 by Baird in Britain and Charles Jenkins in the U.S., the number of scanning lines varying from 30 to 60. Bearing in mind that none of the television broadcast systems now in use has less than 405 lines, the reader can easily imagine how crude Baird's pictures were. Baird himself was eventually converted to electronic scanning after years of experimenting with the alternatives.

The B.B.C. began the first experimental TV service in the world in 1929, using Baird's mechanical scanning. The major problem, once the poor quality of the pictures had been accepted, was that of bandwidth. The range of frequencies occupied by any signals is proportional to the amount of information which they contain, and in the case of television signals this is proportional to the number of lines into which the pictures have been dissected and to the number of pictures per second. The B.B.C. was obliged at the time to transmit on 261 metres (a little more than 1 megacycle/second) and only 12½ images per second were transmitted, for half-hour periods on five days of the week. There was little public interest in these transmissions and sales of the Baird receivers remained small even though they came down in price from about £40 in 1929 to about £20 in 1931. Only a very small proportion of the many thousands of amateurs who had helped to develop and improve the techniques of radio transmission and reception took much interest in television.

After the invention of the iconoscope and the image dissector, most engineers working on television were convinced of the superiority of electronic methods. In Britain, a decisive step was taken with the production of the Emitron camera, based on the iconoscope. An official B.B.C. television service was opened at Alexandra Palace, one of the highest points in North London in November 1936, using the Baird mechanical system and the Marconi-EMI electronic tube system alternately. In the same year RCA opened an experimental television station on top of the Empire State Building in New York, using a system based on the work done by Zworykin and a large team of engineers engaged in perfecting the iconoscope and television circuits. In 1937 a committee of experts in Britain voted in favour of the Marconi-EMI electronic system, with Emitron cameras and cathode-ray tube receivers, and regular programmes were transmitted by the B.B.C. until the outbreak of war.

Most of the basic technical problems in broadcasting television were solved by 1940, but the standards which were then accepted in the quality of transmission and reception would seem very crude today. Pre-war viewers were obliged to huddle over a 6-inch picture in the gloom of a darkened room in order to appreciate whatever entertainment was provided. 'Technical hitches' in the transmitters and studios caused frequent interruptions in programmes and receivers were both expensive and unreliable. Yet such was the fascination of this new medium, at first restricted to trivial and sometimes puerile programme material, that there was a steadily increasing demand for receiving sets in the London area which was abruptly terminated by the war.

The history of television contrasts significantly with the history of radio. Radio was conceived essentially as a means of communication and it was well established in that field before its use for entertainment became popular. Television grew rapidly as a medium of mass entertainment and its application to communications came later. The reason for this is primarily a technical one: bandwidth. Radio requires about 5 kilocycles for adequate transmission of sound but television requires about 5 megacycles because about 1,000 times as many bits of information must be dealt with in the same time. Consequently, whereas radio communication channels could be linked up by telephone networks or land lines with limited bandwidth, television could not, and special techniques had to be developed for an 'entertainment' network, using very high frequencies, which would not infringe on the communication network then in existence. Remembering that very high frequency radio waves tend to behave like light waves, television transmitting and receiving aerials had to be designed on a line-of-sight basis. The B.B.C. had an advantage in this respect since a circle of twenty-five miles radius from Alexandra Palace enclosed nearly one quarter of the whole population of England. The situation was very different in the continental U.S.A. but the American radio industry, especially RCA, had invested many millions of dollars in the commercial prospects of entertainment television and spared no effort in building up a chain of microwave relay links and in developing wide-band co-axial cable for widespread distribution of television broadcasting. A.T. & T. engineers produced a co-axial cable which could carry several hundred telephone conversations at once, and this type of cable was used in 1947 to transmit television between New York, Philadelphia and Washington, but it was expensive and the main distribution of the American television networks was by short-range microwave relay. Directional aerials and amplifiers were fitted on poles about twenty miles apart, sited so as to be higher than intervening objects.

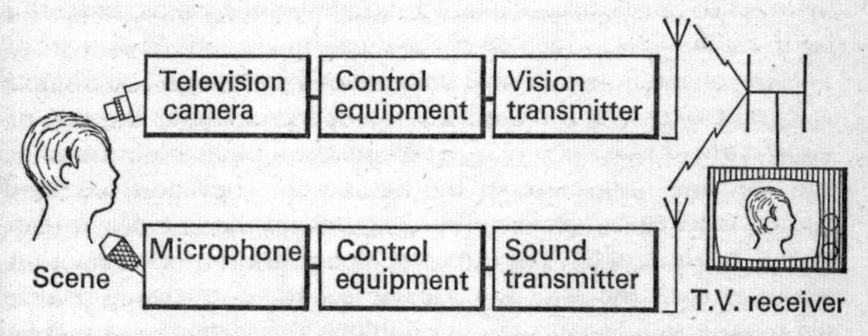


*Figure 41.* The elements of a television broadcasting system.

If the war held up the expansion of television broadcasting for five years, it also provided the research and operational experience required to perfect the techniques of television. The concentration of the best brains in America and Britain on war-time radar produced the greatly improved V.H.F. amplifiers and tuned circuits, the improved miniature valves and components, which were the basis of television receivers after the war. The intensive development of radarscope displays led to marked advances in the technology of cathode-ray tubes: better phosphors were introduced to increase the brightness of the display and electrode assemblies were improved to give increased sensitivity, better focusing and speed of response. Since the performance of a radar system depended on the design and accuracy of pulse and timing circuits these were extensively studied and tried and provided the know-how for the synchronization circuits of the later television systems. Camera, studio and transmission equipment made less progress during the war, but the growth of the electronic industry and the post-war developments in electronics which are described in Chapter 3 ensured that lost time was more than made up.

### TELEVISION BROADCASTING

In the twenty years since the end of the Second World War the rate of expansion of broadcast television has exceeded even that of the cinema. Transmissions can now be received in eighty-five countries. The tall television towers – the world's tallest structures – thrust their antennae into the skies over cities, mountains, forests and plains. Marvels of modern engineering they stand like sentinels of the electronic age, vibrating with the winds, radiating the invisible waves which carry the sights and sounds of the world. These transmissions can now be received by close on 150 million television receivers, but their number is increasing at the rate of more than 10 million a year. (It is interesting that both the total and the rate of growth in the number of television receivers approximate to the corresponding figures for the number of telephone subscribers.) The greatest concentration of television receivers is in the U.S.A. with one set for every three people (65 million sets); in Britain (14 million) and Canada (5 million) there is one for every four people; in Japan (15 million) one for every six. In these countries practically every family has a television receiver or ready access to one and the same situation will soon be reached in the countries of Western Europe. The U.S.S.R. with over 12 million receivers is stepping up their rate of production: 2·9 million were produced in 1964.

There is thus a total potential audience for all television broadcasts in the national networks of more than 500 million. If a global satellite system proceeds according to plan and cooperation can be achieved on a world-scale, it will be possible within five years for more than 1,000 million people of all nations – one-third of the whole human race – to see simultaneously an event in any part of the world while it is happening. Some of my readers may regard this prospect with dismay rather than with satisfaction and they may be consoled by the knowledge that in vast areas of Asia and Africa no television services are yet available. According to

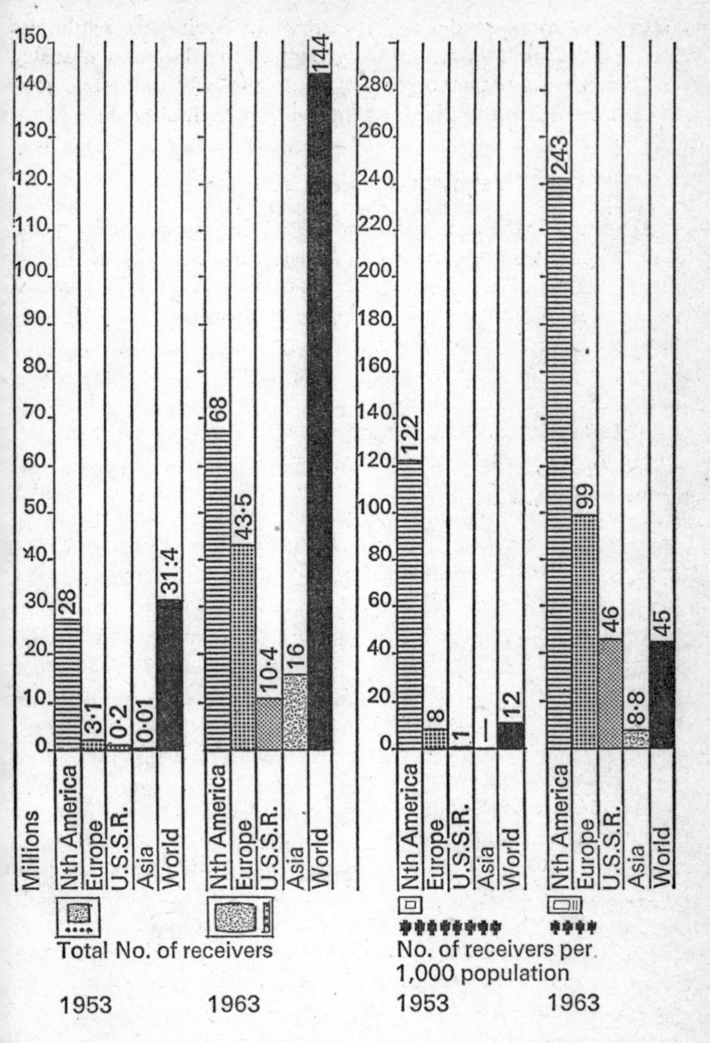


*Figure 42.* Growth in the number of television receivers and the number per 1,000 population in the ten-year period 1953–63. Figures taken from U.N. Statistical Year Books for 1964, 1965.

recent estimates (1965) China has less than a quarter of a million television receivers for her huge population although the highest annual number of cinema attendances in the world is on the Chinese mainland and I have no doubt that it contains potentially the largest television audience in the world as well. For the real videophobe the ideal country at the moment would appear to be India which has only a few thousand receivers. But those who seek to escape television may not be safe from the inexorable march of progress for long. Portable television receivers, using transistors in place of valves, are already on the market. The last technical hurdle to be cleared is a 'solid-state' substitute for the cathode-ray tube or, until this is found, some sort of picture tube with a very low power consumption. Once the television receiver is freed from the mains electricity supply and can operate for reasonable periods from dry batteries the television towers will spring up in the undeveloped parts of the world where no electric power cables have yet appeared.

## MODERN TELEVISION TECHNOLOGY

Although entertainment and advertising now fills the television screens of the world for much of the time (and this will be the subject of discussion in another chapter) we are just beginning to appreciate the tremendous power of this new medium in the dissemination of information, in scientific and industrial research, in politics and government, in education, in medicine, in sport, in space exploration, in production, in transport, banking, commerce . . . in practically every sphere of human activity. For television is an enormous extension and multiplication of the human eye: in space, time, frequency range, sensitivity and reliability. Of course a great amount of research and development in electronics was needed before television attained the remarkable performance of which it is capable today.

The invention of Zworykin's iconoscope and Farnsworth's image dissector in the 1920s triggered off research into camera tubes. In England, an EMI research team, led by Shoenberg and Blumlein, followed up the iconoscope with an improved camera tube, the Emitron, which was patented in 1932. Marconi-EMI was formed in 1934, joining the Marconi company's experience in the transmission of facsimile pictures on short waves with the EMI know-how of the Emitron. Television broadcasting, starting in 1936 as described above, soon produced improvements in the iconoscope and the Emitron, and in the high definition television transmission and reception techniques required to ensure commercial success.

Just prior to the war the ortho-iconoscope, or orthicon, was evolved. This overcame the effects of secondary electron emission in the iconoscope and had a markedly better performance. Just after the war, the R.C.A. engineers developed the image orthicon which combined certain features of the orthicon, the image dissector, and the electron multiplier to give a camera tube 100 to 1,000 times more sensitive than the orthicon so that it could be used for outdoor cameras without the need for any special lighting. The image orthicon was generally adopted in television cameras for entertainment and live television. The amplifiers and auxiliary circuits for television cameras were steadily improved from 1950 onward and the introduction of transistors and solid-state devices made them more compact, more efficient, and more portable. The modern image orthicon camera is not only thousands of times more sensitive than the early iconoscopes, but it is much smaller, much easier to operate and is readily adapted to schemes for automatic operation in television studios and in mobile equipment.

A significant extension of the electronic eye was the invention and development of the vidicon in the last decade. This is a camera tube in which the optical image is translated into a pattern of electrical charges, varying in density, on the surface of a photoconductor made from one of the new semiconducting materials. The surface is then scanned by a low-velocity beam of electrons which converts the charge pattern into a fluctuating current. Physicists and television engineers in America, Britain, Holland and Germany made important contributions to a series of improved vidicons which are now available as extremely compact, sensitive, and very rugged camera tubes. Together with modern circuit techniques and solid-state devices vidicon tubes, perhaps 1½ inches in diameter, make possible television cameras weighing less than 10 lb. which can be made completely waterproof and will withstand the most arduous conditions. Instruments such

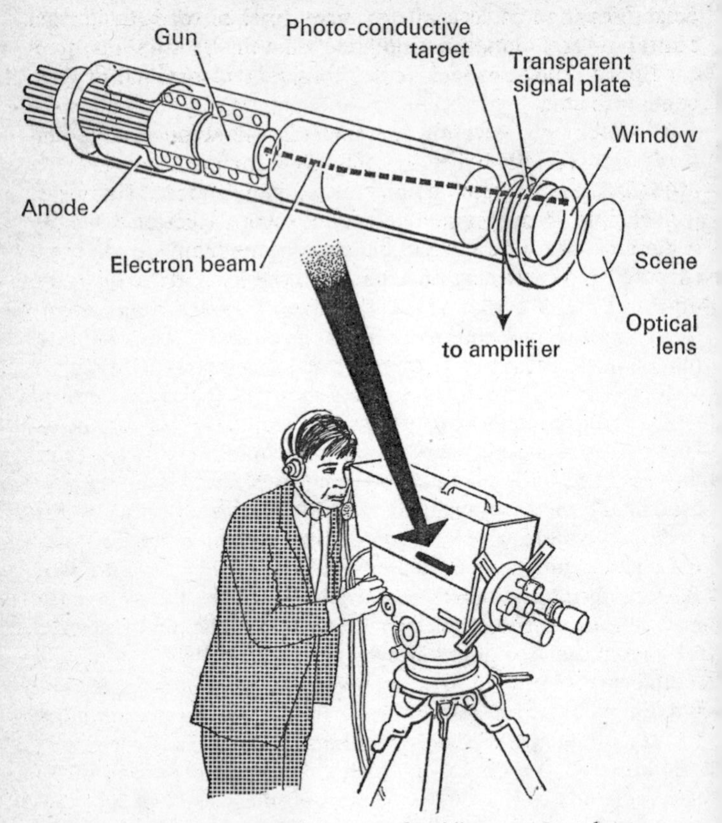


*Figure 43.* Simplified diagram of a vidicon camera tube.

as these, which will function almost anywhere, in conjunction with modern electronic techniques for amplification, control, lens zooming, synchronization, video-tape recording and telemetry have provided the universal eye of television. They have shown us the far side of the moon and the marvellous close-ups of the moon's surface which the Ranger series of missiles sent back to the earth. Nuclear engineers use them to look into the radioactive heart of an atomic reactor with perfect safety, or to supervise the whole complex instrumentation of the plant without leaving their desks. They can be used for the surveillance of road traffic from central control points or mounted on vehicles to study road conditions. They can look round corners, underground or deep beneath the sea.

Closed-circuit television, in which the television camera and receiver are directly linked by cables, is becoming as much a part of modern industry and commerce as the telephone. It is used, for example, to supervise a colliery, a supermarket or a railway station. In large halls and buildings conferences can be made more effective and interesting and lectures more instructive. All parts of a huge liner can be surveyed at any time, from the bridge or any other selected observation points. One can now buy, for little more than the cost of a good cine camera, a miniature television camera which can be connected to a domestic television receiver, so that baby watching can take place from the living-room.

The spectral range of television cameras can be made to extend into the infra-red and the ultra-violet, so that they can see in the dark or reproduce images which could be invisible or harmful to the naked eye. They can be designed with a 'memory' much longer than the retina of the eye, just as the display tubes can be designed to retain a fleeting image for several hours. X-ray screening and photography; infra-red photography of furnace plant or the continuous processing of steel; large screen display of microscopic structures or remote observation of microscopic organisms in vivo; high speed photography; astronomical photography; these are some of the things which can be done with television technique.

# 6

# Faster than Thought

> Is not life a hundred times too short for us
> to bore ourselves?
> Friedrich Nietzsche: *Jenseits von Gut und Böse*

COMPUTERS (nowadays the adjective 'electronic' seems hardly necessary) have caught the imagination of the public. It is very easy to treat them in a sensational manner and phrases such as 'electronic brains' have led some people to endow them with almost magical powers, yet their real power has been, if anything, underestimated. Although much skill, experience and money goes into the construction and exploitation of these machines, there is nothing mysterious about them, and their remarkable performance is based on principles which are not difficult to understand.

Computers are machines for solving problems. Theoretically, any of the problems solved by computers could also be solved by human calculators but the computers are very much faster and never get bored, and the humans may have a better use for their time. Mechanical calculators were designed in the seventeenth century by Pascal and Leibnitz, but lack of engineering skill in their construction made them erratic and inefficient. The nineteenth-century calculating engines of Babbage were a big advance, and the modern mechanical office calculator has reached a high degree of proficiency. But the best and fastest mechanical calculator cannot achieve a hundredth of the speed of a modern digital computer. It was the great speed of operation made possible by electronic techniques which led to the rapid development of computers at the end of the last war as a means of providing quick solutions to the problems posed by the design and operation of military equipment. For example, although highly developed mechanical aids to computing were available in 1940, these were not fast enough for such problems as aiming a gun on the moving platform of a battleship so that it would fire a shell to intercept a high speed aircraft in flight. The first electronic digital computer which worked satisfactorily, ENIAC (Electronic Numerical Integrator and Computer), was built in 1946 by the Moore School of Engineering at the University of Pennsylvania to solve ballistic problems.

## HOW COMPUTERS WORK

There are two main types of electronic computer: analogue and digital. In analogue computers problems are solved by analogy: where the problems involve such quantities as mechanical forces, speeds, rotations, displacements, etc., these are accurately represented in the computer by smoothly varying electrical currents or voltages which can be more conveniently manipulated. Analogue computers tend to be used for scientific and engineering problems in which great accuracy is not required but reasonably accurate answers are needed quickly. A slide rule is a simple example of an analogue computer: distances along the rule are proportional to the logarithms of the quantities which we wish to represent instead of to the quantities themselves.

In digital computers problems are solved by counting, and included in this category are the very large and powerful machines which get into the headlines. All the data connected with the problem to be solved is converted into trains of electrical pulses by very fast electronic switches, and it is these pulses which are marshalled, stored and counted. With modern electronic devices a single switching operation can take place in a few nanoseconds (a nanosecond is a thousand-millionth of a second) so that by converting digits into a series of very short pulses, addition of 10-figure numbers can be carried out in a microsecond and multiplication – which is repeated addition – in a few microseconds.

There are five main units in a digital computer: an input unit which accepts the data, a memory unit for storing and holding the information until it is required, an arithmetical unit which carries out the arithmetical or logical operations on the data according to a set of coded instructions, an output unit for recording or displaying the results of the arithmetical operations, and a control unit which coordinates the operations of the other units.

Most digital computers operate with numbers in the binary system although their inputs can be made to accept numbers in

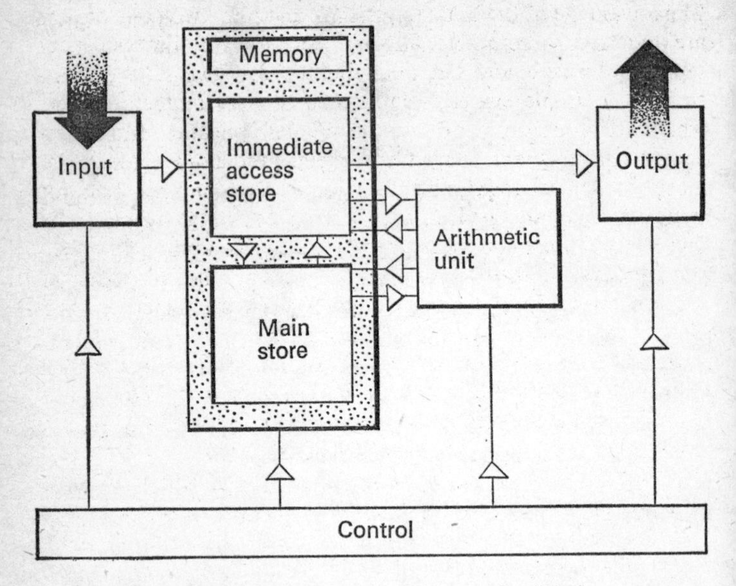


*Figure 44.* A block diagram of the main units of a digital computer.

the decimal system and their output units to convert the results in binary back into the decimal system. In the binary system of numbering there are only two ciphers: 0 and 1. The numbers 0 to 10 in the decimal system are represented as follows:

| Decimal | Binary |
|---|---|
| 0 | 0 |
| 1 | 1 |
| 2 | 10 |
| 3 | 11 |
| 4 | 100 |
| 5 | 101 |
| 6 | 110 |
| 7 | 111 |
| 8 | 1000 |
| 9 | 1001 |
| 10 | 1010 |

The advantage of the binary system is that only two-state devices are required to represent any number; one of the two states representing zero and the other unity. Now two-state devices, such as a simple switch, relay, valve or semiconductor diode, which are either on or off, are the simplest, cheapest and fastest components available. This far outweighs the disadvantages that more of them are required to represent a given number than, for example, ten-state devices for decimal counting. This is why digital computers consist mainly of very large numbers of two-state devices and the processes taking place are the rapid changes in these devices from one state to the other in ordered groups and chains.

In modern digital computers the memory or store is usually a collection of a large number of tiny magnets which have two distinct magnetic states, one representing zero and the other unity. One state is converted very rapidly into the other by an electrical pulse and each little magnet is identified by a number called the 'address'. The control unit, consisting of a collection of electronic switches, selects numbers from the store according to a set of instructions and manipulates them as required by the calculation. The skill in using the computer is mainly in devising the best and most economical programme: i.e. setting up a series of instructions in the language which the machine understands which cause it to carry out all necessary operations in simple steps each specifying a single arithmetic operation. An instruction might be: 'Add number in address 615 to number in address 670', or 'Repeat previous instruction'.

The instructions are carried out in the arithmetic unit, which is made up of a number of electronic circuits which serve as registers and are termed accumulators. When presented with the first instruction quoted above the operation is to read the contents of address 615 into the accumulator, and then read the contents of address 670 into the accumulator; the total in the accumulator is then read out to another address in the store, leaving the accumulator free for the next operation. Arithmetic units are capable of addition, multiplication, subtraction and division and elementary logical operations.

Suppose, for example, that the manager of a shirt factory asks his computer: 'Have we enough buttons for last week's shirt production?'. The computer has the total number of shirts produced last week in its store as well as the total number of buttons in stock. It is programmed to calculate the number of buttons required and to compare this number (a) with the number (b) in the appropriate address for buttons in stock. If (a) is less than (b) it answers 'Yes'. If (a) is greater than (b) it answers 'No'. The uninitiated might imagine that this is all very well for shirts and buttons but it is much too simple-minded an approach for the solution of some abstruse mathematical equation or some complex scientific problem. If so, they would be wrong. Every problem which is soluble can be broken down into these elementary logical operations. It might be very tedious to solve them that way, and some problems might take teams of mathematicians months of work with pencil and paper slogging away at never-ending but simple sums. But the computer is in its element with this kind of work and keeps up its tremendous pace indefinitely. Errors *can* occur in computer working but they are usually glaring ones which are easily spotted.

Data, or information, is supplied to the computer through the input unit and may take many forms. These include punched paper tape, punched cards, magnetic tape, magnetic cards, signals from electric typewriters, data transmitted by wire, among others. Whatever the form of the input data the input unit must translate the information into digital electronic signals when the programme asks for it. Modern high-speed digital computers have tremendous appetites for information and there has been much research and effort in devising ways of feeding in data quickly and accurately. Various attempts have been made by British and American designers to fit reading machines to computer inputs so that information may be read directly from original documents. One of the most successful of these so far is the 'Autolector', a British designed reading machine which reads computer-printed or handwritten forms straight into a computer store at the rate of 14,000 items per hour. An experimental computer designed in America will accept verbal instructions.

The output unit may also be required to deliver the processed information in various forms. The three main direct methods of output are punched paper tape, punched cards and magnetic tape and each of these can be used to activate printing mechanisms.

Printing mechanisms, which must be capable of high speeds, include electric typewriters, line-at-a-time type printers and electrostatic printers. Input and output units may be sited in proximity to the other units, or the data may be acquired from, and the output distributed to, numerous distant locations. Electronic data processing systems comprise all the peripheral equipment as well as the central computer or computers.

## EVOLUTION OF ELECTRONIC COMPUTERS

In the twenty years or so since work was started on the design of the early electronic computers we can discern several stages of development. The first computers were really laboratory devices and they tended to fill the whole of any laboratory in which they were constructed. ENIAC, completed in 1946, fills a large room in the Ballistics Research Laboratories in Aberdeen, Maryland. It has no less than 18,000 thermionic valves and consumes 100 kilowatts of power so that one could cook a hot dinner in it while calculating firing tables. EDSAC I (Electronic Delay Storage Automatic Computer) was built at Cambridge in 1949 under the direction of Dr M. V. Wilkes, F.R.S. It had only 3,000 valves but was six times as fast as ENIAC. ACE (Automatic Computing Engine) was completed at the National Physical Laboratory in 1951 after six years of work based on a design from first principles by Dr Turing. A second version of ACE was in operation at the N.P.L. in 1958, when it was one of the world's biggest and fastest computers.

These early computers were used for scientific work but they served as prototypes for the 'first generation' of commercial computers. The first of the commercial machines was derived from EDSAC I and was called LEO (Lyons Electronic Office). It was built in 1953 by J. Lyons and Co. for their head office and made a major contribution to the efficient running of the Lyons' teashops for twelve years.

The English Electric DEUCE (Digital Electronic Universal Computing Engine) was based on the original ACE; DEUCE Mk I was designed for engineering and scientific applications and DEUCE Mk II formed the central unit for a number of data processing systems. The Americans were somewhat slower to build computers for commercial applications but, once started, they built them in much larger numbers than the British. It is characteristic of the pattern of technical development since 1920 that British scientists and engineers were in the forefront of computer design by 1950, but by 1960 American companies had established a dominant position in the manufacture and sale of computers to the rest of the world and today they have captured a substantial part of the market in Britain itself.

In Britain the construction and sales of digital computers were undertaken by two groups of firms from the office equipment and electronics sectors of industry respectively. The manufacturers of office equipment, calculating machines, punched cards, etc., included Burroughs, British Tabulating Machine (Hollerith), Power Samas, National Cash Register, I.B.M. United Kingdom, Remington Rand and De La Rue Bull Machines which was a tie-up between the British firm De La Rue and the French Machines Bull. The British Tabulating Machine and Power Samas were the first of the firms to merge and formed International Computers and Tabulators Ltd; this process of concentration of resources and merging of smaller groups into larger ones became typical of the computer business in America, Britain and the Continent and there are very few small firms left in today. The second group of firms, from the electronics side, included: Ferranti, Elliott Brothers, Standard Telephone and Cables, EMI Electronics, English Electric and A.E.I.

In America the computer became a status symbol for many businesses and during the 1950s high-pressure selling was responsible for putting digital computers into many organizations which were not prepared for the upheaval which was often entailed. Not only the customers and users but the manufacturers of computers as well had a great deal to learn and the first generation of computers had their full share of the 'teething trouble' which is associated with radically new developments. The electronics industry was turning out much-improved valves and components but they were still not quite good enough to meet the very exacting requirements of machines in which one component failure out of many thousands might mean a very expensive hold-up. However, some American businesses were quick to learn that with proper consultation between makers and users, and systematic planning of the way in which they would be used, these machines were very effective and soon repaid their capital costs in increased efficiency. The existence of a large and growing home market for scientific, industrial and business computers in the U.S.A. was the basis for the rapid expansion of firms such as International Business Machines, Honeywell and Remington Rand in this field and by the end of the fifties they had acquired the experience and know-how which was to be their greatest asset in their attack on world markets.

But in Britain, apart from the scientists and a small progressive minority of industrialists, the new electronic machines were treated with suspicion and the Government was either ignorant of or indifferent to their implications. By the end of 1960 not more than about 300 computers had been delivered to users in the U.K. and Britain was at least five years behind the Americans in the practical application of these machines.

With the beginning of the sixties came the 'second generation' of computers. These not only embodied the experience of the previous decade but made radical departures in the use of new components, assembly techniques and design philosophies. Thermionic valves were replaced by transistors and semiconductor devices, with consequent sharp reduction in size, power consumption and heat dissipation; the jungles of wires for internal connexions were largely eliminated by the use of printed circuit techniques and plug-in units on standardized boards; the new ferrite materials were used in extremely compact, high-capacity, magnetic storage devices with very short access time to individual storage elements. With improved switching devices and circuits the speed of operation increased – in fact modern computers are so fast that the time taken for signals travelling at the speed of light along the internal connexions is already a limiting factor in the performance.

In the last five years the use of computers by all industrialized nations has grown rapidly. The American Management Association estimated that, by the end of 1964, 21,000 machines were in operation in the U.S.A., most of these being general-purpose machines renting at between $10,000 and $25,000 a year. The total potential computing capacity of such a number of machines must be enormous, but the A.M.A. considered that only a very small proportion of the computers installed in America were being used to their full capacity and that many were incorrectly used. Some experts considered that the much smaller number of installations in Britain at the time – just under 1,000 – were better managed than the American machines, particularly in the application of computers to industrial processes, but Britain had fallen a long way behind not only America but most of Western Europe as far as numbers were concerned. By 1965, Switzerland had three times as many computers per million of working population as Britain, and Sweden and France twice as many. Norway, West Germany, Holland, Denmark, Belgium and Italy were also ahead of Britain on this rating. Japan had developed her own computer industry and was competing with America and Britain for world markets. The Japanese were not simply making cheap copies of American and British equipment but were doing their own research and development and making original contributions to the computer art.

I have not been able to obtain reliable figures as to the number of computers in the U.S.S.R., but there is no doubt that the Soviet Government attaches great importance to the production and exploitation of computers. In an article in *Pravda*, the Communist Party newspaper, of 17 January 1965, Mr Nikolai Federenko, a Soviet industrial expert, said that Russia needed a network of computers to carry out her economic plans and that she had the capacity to overtake the West in the effective use of electronics in economic management in the Soviet Union. This appears to be one way of saying that Russia was lagging behind the West in the use of computers, but the Russians have demonstrated their ability to master the most advanced technologies and we may expect to see rapid advances in computer technology in the Soviet Union in the next few years.

A bid to regain Britain's leading position in the world with respect to computers was made by the Labour Government at the beginning of 1965. The Minister of Technology, Mr Cousins, announced a plan in the Commons (1 January 1965) to create a rapid increase in the use of computers and computer techniques in industry and commerce. The plan was based on a 'flourishing British computer industry' which would consist of the firms: A.E.I., A.T.E. (Plessey), Elliotts, English Electric, Ferranti,

G.E.C. and I.C.T. The American-owned firms producing computers in Britain included: Burroughs, Digital Equipment Corporation, Electronic Associates, Honeywell, I.B.M. and Standard Telephones and Cables. A review of the computer requirements of universities, colleges of advanced technology and research councils had been started and would lead to a new five-year programme of procurement, starting with an amount of £2 million annually. Another £1 million was ear-marked for programmes of research into advanced computer techniques by the industry, Government research establishments and the Post Office. The plan included the formation of a computer advisory unit to advise on requirements throughout the public sector and a proposal to establish a national computer centre which would acquire programmes from computer makers and users and form a library. This belated recognition by a British government of the importance of the computer industry, which will play a key role in the second industrial revolution, may do something to improve Britain's position in relation to America and the countries of Western Europe. But it is significant that the expenditure on computers planned by the Government is trifling compared with, for instance, that for the aviation industry. I think that computers will prove to be more important to Britain than supersonic aircraft. For one thing, they will be required for the design, testing and operation of those aircraft. They could even be used to show whether such aircraft will be economic.

## MAMMOTHS VERSUS MODULES

As we draw near the end of the period of the 'second generation' of computers we can observe an interesting dichotomy in their evolution. The monsters of the 'first generation' have given way to their much more compact and efficient cool-running successors, but the leading computer firms in America, Britain, Japan, France and Holland have all had aspirations to build bigger and better models with the new parts which would have an altogether higher order of capacity and speed than their giant predecessors. There are many arguments in favour of large units. One very powerful argument is that although the capital cost of these mammoths is very large, running into millions of pounds, they have such

*'This is operative 37639481, and this — this is A.L.F.I.E.*

*Figure 45.* Reproduced by permission of *Punch.*

tremendous speed and capacity that the cost *per calculation* in a given time is less than it is for the much smaller and cheaper machines. Scientists, in particular, are making urgent demands for very powerful and rapid computing facilities to solve problems in nuclear physics, astrophysics, molecular biology, mathematical theory and many other disciplines which involve vast amounts of calculation. The alternative approach to computer design is the 'modular' system. All the basic units of the computer – storage units, arithmetical units, input units, etc. – are standardized and designed so that they can be added on to existing assemblies. Users then build up their equipment to whatever capacity they need by simply plugging in new modules or unplugging any modules not required.

The first of the mammoths was the I.B.M. 7030 nicknamed STRETCH, designed to be the biggest and best machine of its day capable of more than one million logical operations per second. Several models of STRETCH were completed but its performance never came up to expectations and certainly did not justify the millions of pounds which it cost. The disappointing performance of STRETCH caused I.B.M. to devote much more attention to the modular alternative and a range of modules were developed which has had considerable success in world markets. In Britain, however, Ferranti went ahead with the design of an even bigger machine than STRETCH, namely ATLAS. ATLAS has a very impressive specification. It can accept one million instructions per second. Its working store contains up to 256×4,096 words of 48 bits. The main store comprises 4 or more magnetic drums of 24,000 words. It will read punched cards at the rate of 600 per minute and print out results at the rate of 600 lines per minute. The facility known as time-sharing enables it to handle any number of operations concurrently, without any possibility that an error in one of them will interfere with another. It has a supervisory routine in its fixed store which will review the priorities of programmes from time to time and adjust them to ensure the most efficient working of the system as a whole. Four consoles allow independent access to four users, each of whom may be running more than one programme at a time.

The first ATLAS prototype was completed in 1961 and installed at Manchester University. Ferranti were satisfied with the performance of the prototype and although there was some trouble with the 'hardware' (the fashionable term for the physical bits which make up the central computer and its store) it provided a very badly needed service for many scientific research teams in various parts of the country. The Institute of Computer Science was formed by London University and ordered an ATLAS – cost about £2 million – which was to be their main tool. Unfortunately for the reputation of the world's most advanced computer a host of technical problems was encountered and the manufacturers, I.C.T. who had bought Ferranti's interest, were still battling with these in March 1965, one year after the university was expected to have full use of the installation. Frustrated would-be users found that the machine was working only four or five hours a day and getting through several hundred jobs instead of the several thousand anticipated. Some research projects had to be scrapped or diverted elsewhere; for instance, an Imperial College scheme to analyse large numbers of nuclear physics results by direct link with ATLAS was abandoned and an American machine in Germany had to be used instead.

The trouble was not with the hardware but with the 'software', in particular with the supervisory routine, which represented a task of much greater magnitude than had been appreciated. An important factor which should have been well understood after American experience was the necessity for the greatest possible cooperation between manufacturer's design and development staff and the Institute's staff, whereas in fact this seems to have been inadequate. The problems of ATLAS may well be solved eventually and it will then represent a very big advance in the computer art. Or it may be that the more flexible approach with modular construction may get quicker results and the mammoths may turn out to be white elephants.

## THE SHAPE OF COMPUTERS TO COME

The 'third generation' of computers began to appear while this book was being written. The hardware for these is based on the 'micromodule' technique and the integrated circuits described in Chapter 3. They are much more compact assemblies than present designs and will become more compact still. A central computer with its store housed in a single cabinet could have the capacity of an ATLAS which now fills a large office. This will still leave the problems of the 'software' and peripheral equipment. I think that very marked advances will be made in the former and that the latter may well decide the overall size and cost of an installation, especially for commercial purposes. Among the improvements made to match the speeds of input and output equipment to that of the central computer will be automatic reading devices which will be able to read directly from handwriting or print into the computer store, as well as input devices which will translate spoken instructions into machine language.

The present early developments in building up computer centres with line links to users will expand into computer networks on a regional and national scale. These complex and powerful installations will be serviced and maintained by specially designed computers. This will enable the computer power of a whole nation such as Britain to be coordinated and used to the best advantage. A big step towards this goal will be made when a universal machine language for computers has been perfected and accepted so that programmes can be executed with the maximum efficiency by all computers in the network.

After micromodules, the application of microelectronics (see Chapter 3) to data processing equipment will lead to pocket computers which could become as familiar to the scientists and engineers of the future as the slide rule is now.

There has been a great deal of discussion about whether machines can be designed to think for themselves. While present-day computers do not do this, since they are told what to think, I cannot see any fundamental reason why artificial structures cannot be designed to simulate the processes of thought. Indeed there is evidence that this has recently been done. The United States Air Force announced in April 1965 that it had made a rudimentary model of a machine capable of learning from its own mistakes. The function of a nerve cell was created artificially in a device called an artron (artificial neuron) which, in clusters, had a memory and could solve problems. An Air Force Systems Command spokesman said that a network of artrons wired together 'respond to punishment and reward by learning desired behaviour and capitalizing on their own mistakes. They make decisions and actively seek new and better ways of doing a given task. Knock out some of the artron tools for doing that task and it will dream up an altogether different approach for accomplishing the same thing.' The Air Force's interest in this device is in developing a system of flight control which will not have to be programmed in advance, will be reliable for long periods capable of functioning after some elements have failed, and able to adapt itself to unforeseen conditions. They considered that their apparatus would be ready for use within ten years, and would be able to find solutions even if there was a seventy per cent electronic failure. Techniques such as this in conjunction with future developments in microelectronics will create electronic brains which may rival our own in some respects.

In the next twenty years computers will undoubtedly take over more and more of the paper work, the routine and repetitive operations of modern life. This will happen in industry, in commerce, and in local and national government administration and services. What will happen to the clerks and the white collar workers as the computers take over? This is only one of the problems posed by the electronic revolution and I shall return to it later. What I think can hardly be disputed is that very far-reaching social changes will be brought about by computers whether we are prepared for them or not.

# 7

# Electronics and the Second Industrial Revolution

> If we look hopefully upon the shape of things to come, we can visualize automation as the greatest blessing mankind has ever known. Albert Einstein

THE first industrial revolution replaced human muscles in industry by steam and mechanical power. The second industrial revolution will replace manual control in industry with electronic control. If this new revolution seems less dramatic now than the political revolutions of our time, its effects on the way we live, like those of the first industrial revolution, will be much greater in the long run. Man does not live by technology alone but his material welfare is eventually determined by it. Our civilization would be a poor thing indeed without our highly developed political and social organization, without the humanities, art, music, philosophy – but it would perish altogether without our technology since we would revert to the level of naked savages, doomed to starve or freeze to death if the environment became unfavourable. It is precisely his unique ability to exercise conscious control over his material environment which makes man the dominant species on our planet. Electronics gives us the technical means for an enormous extension of this control. It offers the prospect of effortless control of the immense stores of energy locked in the earth or radiated by the sun. It provides the basis for the automatic production of all the goods we need. Electronics is the key to automation.

## MECHANIZATION AND AUTOMATION

The word 'automation' is heard and seen very frequently nowadays but experts differ as to its precise meaning. Historically the word was first coined in 1947 by D. S. Harder, a manager in the Ford Motor Company in Detroit, to describe the automatic handling of materials and parts into and out of the transfer machines which thus manufactured car engines without any intervention by machine operators. John Diebold, an American university undergraduate, also invented the word at about the same time to describe 'an exciting new system of making factory production lines almost completely automatic through the use of electronic control systems'. The literal meaning of the word, which is a hybrid from the Greek 'automatos' (self-moving) and the Latin suffix 'ion', is 'self-moving action'. Sir Leon Bagrit, in his 1964 Reith Lectures, tells us that he does not like the word, because of the visions of Frankenstein-like monsters which it conjures up, and would like to replace it with 'cybernation' (another hybrid). But the word has become an accepted part of modern language because, whatever its formal definition, it is popularly used to describe ideas and techniques which have material and visible effects on everyday life and which are growing rapidly in importance. These ideas and techniques include everything – hydraulic, pneumatic, mechanical, electrical, electronic, even bits of string – which makes automatic production more possible; but I think that any definition of automation should emphasize the predominant role of electronic techniques.

The origins of automation can be traced back to the early days of the first industrial revolution with the introduction of mechanization, but one must avoid the common mistake of saying that automation is simply extensive mechanization. Nor would I go to the opposite extreme, with Sir Leon Bagrit, of saying that automation is just the opposite of mechanization, any more than I would describe a living man as the opposite of his skeleton: the second is contained in the first, it is an essential part of it, but it is much less than the whole thing.

The relation between automation and mechanization may be illustrated by a simple example. Consider the manufacture of metal washers. These articles could be made somewhat laboriously from lumps of metal using only hand tools. A better way is to use a machine tool which can stamp out dozens of washers at one stroke from sheet metal fed into it. That is mechanization. The machine is under the control of a machinist who watches the product, perhaps with the aid of measuring and sensing devices, and adjusts the speed of the machine, or the setting, or the supply of raw material if the parts do not come out as required. Now

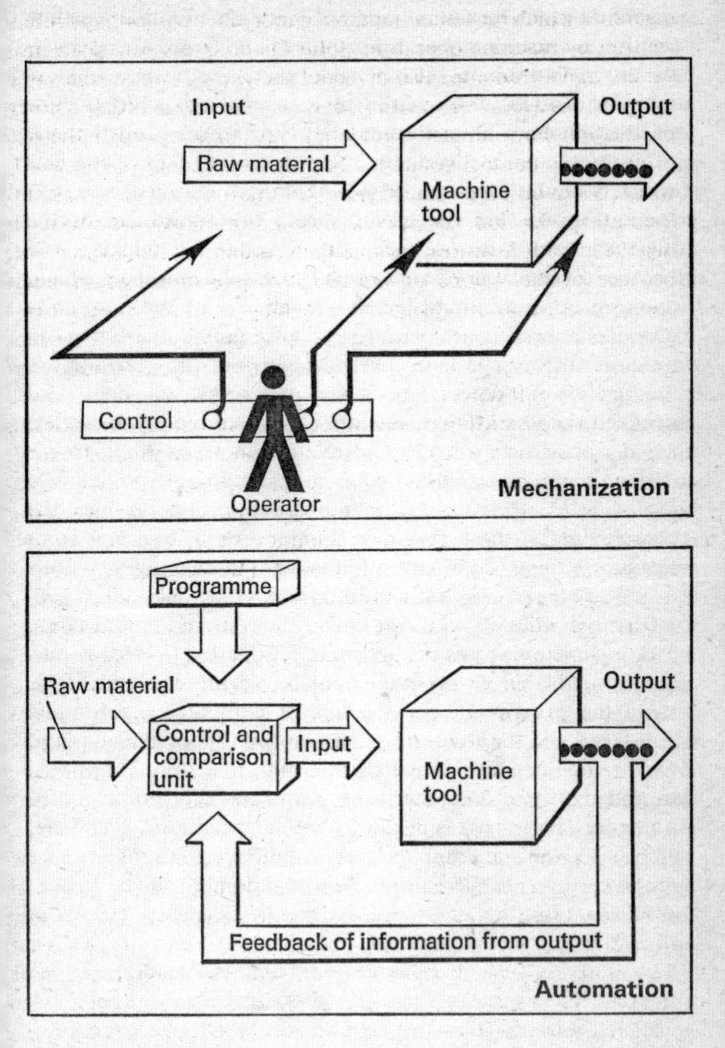


*Figure 46.* The diagrams compare the role of the human operator in mechanization and automation.

suppose that sensing and measuring devices fitted to the machine examine the washers as they are produced and feed back information to an automatic control unit which compares what is happening with what is ordered by a tape carrying instructions for the machine. That is automation. The manual control of the machinist is replaced by the automatic control which operates through a closed loop, as the feedback path is called, and acts continuously to vary the motor speed, the adjustment of the cutters, the rate of flow of metal strip through the machine, and any other controllable variables which affect the finished product.

Now imagine this machine in the context of the automatic factory. The washers are perhaps part of a gear-box assembly in which the factory specializes. All the parts of the gear-box are produced by automatic machines in production lines and assembled automatically in assembly lines. All the raw materials are fed from stores into the production lines according to the commands of a master production control computer which also coordinates the activities of the individual production lines, the assembly lines, inspection and packing stores. The master computer is in two-way communication with all these individual units and is also supplied with the information which determines production: the order book, target dates, material and labour costs, etc. A complete analysis of the whole production process is thus instantly available to production management who amend or change the programme for the master computer accordingly. There is no need for any factory hand in this (hypothetical) plant. Even the maintenance of the plant could, if it were considered desirable, be under computer supervision and servicing could be automatic. This is what is meant by 'full automation'. There are, as far as I know, no completely automatic factories in existence anywhere, although there are some which do not fall far short of full automation, and there are many in which some degree of automation has been introduced.

It will be apparent, even to the non-technical reader, that the automatic factory must depend on the efficient operation of many automatic sensing and measuring devices which effect the automatic control of each unit in the plant and transmit the information to the central control which is necessary for the coordination of all the units. This is where electronic devices come into their

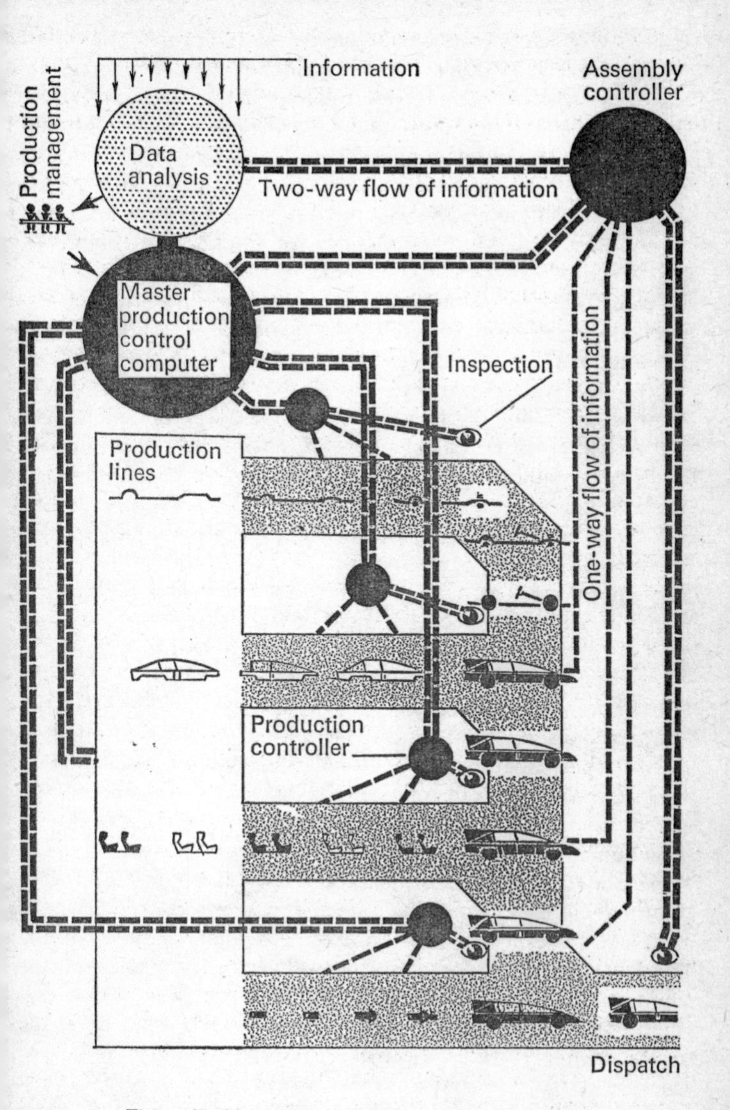


*Figure 47.* An automatic factory (see pages 158–60).

own. It is difficult to name any measurement or property involved in the process of modern production – temperature, pressure, volume, length, velocity, acceleration, weight, colour, vibration, torque, resistance, hardness, and so on – which cannot be converted into the movement of electrons, and so integrated into the process of electronic control. The conversion to electron movement is carried out by a very numerous class of devices known as transducers, which includes the devices described in Chapter 3, and which are now produced in large quantities by the electronics industry. There are other ways of measuring and sensing production operations than with electronic devices but most of these are inferior in speed of response, sensitivity, accuracy and flexibility and they are in many cases unable to match the great speeds of machine members in modern high-speed production. The transmission of the data and measurements from the various parts of the factory to the data-processing equipment and to and from the master computer would represent a formidable problem if electronic techniques were not available. Finally, the vast volume of information which must be processed by the central computer could not be dealt with fast enough by any mechanical calculator. Only the high-speed electronic digital computer can cope with this.

### SOME EXAMPLES OF AUTOMATION IN INDUSTRY

Perhaps the best way to grasp the scope and power of automation is to consider a few real examples from modern industry. Our first example is from the mining industry: coal mining in Britain. Automatic methods of getting coal which will have a profound effect on the future of deep mining were given extensive trials in 1963 and 1964 at two British collieries: Newstead Colliery in Nottingham and Ormonde Colliery in Derbyshire. After many years of preliminary work by scientists and engineers of the National Coal Board and from private industry a solution was found to a problem which should be on the conscience of everyone: that of removing the main dangers to men working at the coal-face in deep seams. Electronic techniques made it possible to cut and convey the coal from the face without the need for any men there. The operating principle of the automatic installation at the two collieries is straightforward. A coal cutter moves along the coal-face, cutting out a slice 20 ins. wide. When it reaches the end it returns, while a plough tips the cut coal on to a conveyor. This transfers the coal to another conveyor at right angles to the first and running under the control console to the loading area. When the cutter and its plough have executed one complete cutting cycle, the whole of the coal cutting and conveying machinery advances another 20 ins. into the seam and the cutter starts the next slice into the coal-face. A means of steering the cutter and plough is provided as well as for removing spilt coal which might impede the conveyor.

A major contribution to the successful operation of the system is the Chock Automation System, an ingenious and safe method of moving the roof supports forward by remote control, which makes use of the latest electronic devices and techniques. Conveyor and chocks are advanced automatically, with snake-like movements, after each run of the coal shearer, and the conditions at the coal-face, or at any chock, are indicated on a central control panel at the main gate. The electronic equipment uses over 1,000 transistors and after three months' working it was found that only one of these had developed a fault.

These automatic installations, which can cut coal at the rate of 4 tons per minute, are now contributing to the normal production of the collieries. They show that coal can be won from deep seams without hazard or discomfort to the miners. There are no technical reasons why they should not be introduced extensively into British mines although there is the human problem of what would happen to the miners who would become redundant if this type of automation were to replace traditional methods of coal-getting.

The next example is taken from a process industry – the production of steel. Advanced automation in the manufacture of steel is now fully operational at the Spencer Steel Works of Richard Thomas & Baldwins at Newport in South Wales, in one of the most modern steel plants in the world. It is based on a system called ARCH – Articulated Computing Hierarchy – developed by the Elliott Automation Group. In this, a control hierarchy of computers operates in parallel with the human organization of the plant personnel so as to retain the usual management structure while augmenting human skills and experience with the great speed and precision of the computers. The enormous amount of information necessary to attain the optimum efficiency in the operation of a plant of this size and complexity could not be dealt with by traditional methods, but the ARCH system allowed the automation plan to be implemented stage by stage so that production could be continued while changes were made.

In the finished system a computer accepts incoming customer orders and computes the steel production schedule. This information is fed to a second computer which controls the ingot slab and breaks the production schedule down into local commands for the steel plant, slab mill and hot strip mill. It also controls transmission of instructions to the plant and receives back details of the production progress from keyboards operated at twenty main production points, and from data which is transmitted automatically by instruments in the plant. The information digested by the second computer is then transmitted to the first, which modifies the original production schedule to take into account the production changes signalled. Under the overall control of what is called a plant scheduler, the computer hierarchy will be linked with other Richard Thomas & Baldwin plants so that optimum production schedules can be prepared for the whole group of companies.

Next, let's take the automatic control of a special kind of machine tool. Machine tools – the machines which make the machines – are the basis of all modern manufacturing operations and Diebold's definition of automation could be interpreted as the electronic control of machine tools forming a transfer line. One of the most difficult and costly operations in engineering is the continuous machining of complex shapes in three dimensions from solid lumps of metal, and the traditional method of making such shapes in quantity is by pressing, forging or die-sinking, using specially made dies. Before 1925 such dies were machined painstakingly by a skilled machinist using a conventional milling machine, but a step forward was made with the introduction of the tracer controlled milling machine. These machines, using electrical sensing devices and servomechanisms, machined the dies accurately and automatically in very hard steel from models in wood, plaster or soft metal. The models were made by a craftsman from an engineering drawing.

The final stage in the automation of this type of process came

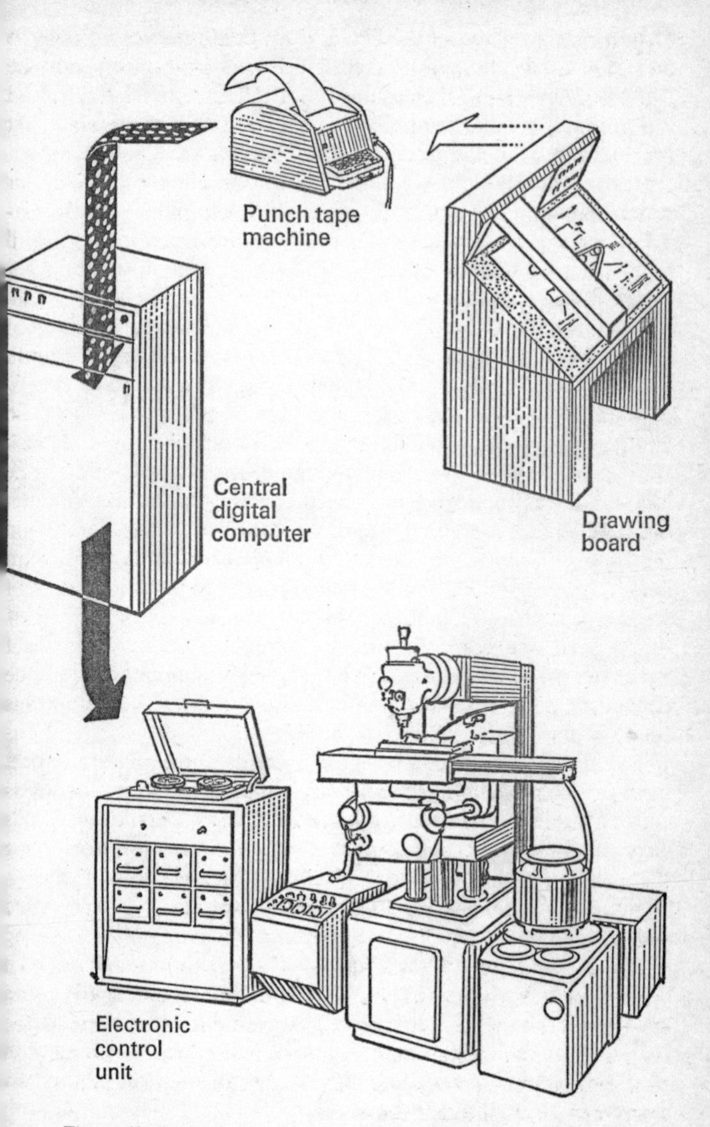


*Figure 48*. Stages in the numerical control of a machine tool.

with the introduction of the Ferranti Mark IV numerical control system towards the end of the 1950s. This system replaces the sequence: drawing – craftsman – model – machinist – machine tool, by a digital computer. The programmer first converts the design data from the drawings into a series of numbers which represent the rectilinear coordinates of a sufficient number of slices through the solid component, together with instructions for the tool feed and speed. These numbers are coded on punched tape which is then read by a digital computer in a computer centre and converted into instructions for the machine on magnetic tape, allowing for up to three hours of machining time from one spool of tape. The tape is fitted on the deck of the electronic control console, which is completely transistorized, and stands beside the machine tool itself. A single on-off switch starts the machining cycle. Hydraulic servo motors, which have sufficient stiffness and power to take advantage of the fast rate of control, follow the instructions from the magnetic tape and move the machine slides accordingly. Optical diffraction gratings along the machine slides monitor the actual position of the tool and send back correcting signals to the controls to compensate for any error in transmission. The machine can of course be programmed to produce one complex part after another or to repeat any particular piece as required. The larger the number of components in a given batch, the greater the saving in machine time and cost compared with a skilled machinist.

The fact that I have taken the foregoing examples of automation from British industry does not imply that Britain is more advanced with automation than other countries. In the particular instances quoted it is probably fair to say that Britain leads the world, but they are not typical of British industry which is proving slow to take advantage of the very advanced electronic control systems now available.

The increasing use of techniques such as those described marks the first stage of the new industrial revolution. The most advanced level of automation has been reached in the process industries – such as steel, petroleum and chemicals – in which raw materials are continuously processed as they flow through the plant and emerge as finished products. It seems probable that in a decade or so these plants will be integrated in thorough-going automation schemes which will include automatic extraction of the raw materials from the earth, automatic processing and automatic distribution of the processed materials to the users. The countries in which process automation is most advanced include the United States, Soviet Union, Britain, Sweden, Germany and France. The power-generating industries, which include nuclear-electric, and hydro-electric power generation, are also going along the same road to automation as the processing of materials. The motor-car industry, especially in America, France and Britain, is now largely based on automatic machining in transfer lines although automatic assembly is less advanced. A considerable degree of automation has also been introduced into the food industry, the bottling industry, the clothing industry, launderies, the plastics industry and others. Electronic control of machine tools is well advanced in the United States; nearly half of the large machine tools now built in the U.S. are numerically controlled. In Britain the proportion is much smaller, despite the excellent control systems developed here. In the Soviet bloc the proportion appears to be small at the moment but it is increasing rapidly.

Automation in the office is most highly developed in America, but electronic data processing – which includes computers and peripheral equipment – is making rapid progress in most European countries and in the U.K., and it looks very much as though the all-electronic office may become general before the automatic factory. However, one should bear in mind that work in the factory and work in the office are becoming more alike with increasing automation.

Automation has also made its impact on many other social activities – transport, communications, education, medicine, for example – but these are discussed in other chapters and I shall not elaborate on them here. The most sceptical reader should be satisfied that the second industrial revolution has really begun. It has already created a number of social, political and economic problems which we will ignore at our peril, and I shall now venture into a discussion of these.

## SOME HUMAN PROBLEMS OF AUTOMATION

Just as there was resistance to the idea of using machines to replace muscle power by all sections of nineteenth-century society, so there is now resistance to the idea of using electronics to replace human control of machines. Some people have very good reason for their fears: those, for instance, who have acquired industrial skills after long apprenticeship, training and practical experience and now find that their jobs can be done by boxes of gadgets. Others have less rational grounds for their objections. One very widespread belief, which I have heard from highly educated as well as from ignorant people, is that men will always be better than machines for many of the jobs in industry.

It has been pointed out by Norbert Wiener, Stafford Beer, and others that the use of men as machine minders is a waste of human material. The human brain is unmatched by any artificial device so far invented in initiative and adaptability, but it is far less suited to the supervision of the repetitive processes of modern industry than electronic devices. It is much slower and far less accurate. A machine minder who thinks of nothing but a specified series – however long or complex – of button pushings and lever pullings on his machine is a very odd human being. Most people have plenty of other things to think about – home, hobbies, sex, politics, music, holidays and what not. The computer thinks about nothing but its programmed operations and forgets nothing relating to them. Electronic devices in the factory never get tired, bored or hungry. They can work perfectly in conditions which human beings would find intolerable.

Then there is a general suspicion of all this 'machinery', especially this complex, *electronic* gadgetry – surely, say the sceptics, it's bound to go wrong. It is true enough that any machine and any electronic device can develop a fault and any system can break down, but so can human beings and it is easier to design for machine fallibility than for the human factor. To get this matter in proportion one should remember that there are some ten thousand million neurons in the human brain and that even a complicated control operation might involve no more than a hundred or so; if more neurons are required to participate in any operation there are normally plenty available, so that if any neuron or group of neurons is unreliable or uncertain in its action, reserve neurons can be called into play as often as necessary. With only a fraction of this amount of redundancy, electronic equipment could be designed with a negligibly small rate of failure. The reader will recall that the microelectronic circuit elements described in Chapter 3 can already be produced so that more than 10,000 can be packed into a space of a cubic inch and replication of circuit elements does not now present any serious difficulties. Automatic control systems which are self-maintaining as well as self-acting are on the horizon. When they arrive, skilled maintenance men are going to be in the same boat with skilled machinists; it is not too soon now to think about where that boat is going.

This ingrained distrust of inanimate systems which act without human guidance is, I think, pretty universal and is responsible both for holding up the application of automation where it is technically and economically desirable and for the incorrect application of it when it is used. The automatic pilot is indispensable for modern aircraft and landing in fog can now be safely executed with automatic landing systems, whereas it can be extremely hazardous if the pilot has to rely on his senses. Yet how many of us would remain unperturbed on a flight without a human pilot?

This reluctance to surrender the entire control of a system to automatic devices is often rationalized, not only by laymen but by managers, engineers and scientists, to justify the use of half-hearted automation. These people point out that since the machines used cannot think for themselves they must therefore always be subject to the intelligent direction and guidance of human beings. It would be better to put this in another way: the goal or objective of any system of automation is set by human beings; engineers and mathematicians design the automatic control system to attain that objective in the most efficient way. Often the technical problem of the design is so complex that no theoretical solution is available and an experimental *self-acting* control system may be used to *find* the best solution and to collect data for theoretical analysis. During the experimental stage, the designers and engineers may interfere at any stage of the process and continuous observations and measurements may be recorded or observed. But once the target has been hit and the control problem solved, any human observation, action or decision used originally can be replaced by more efficient automatic

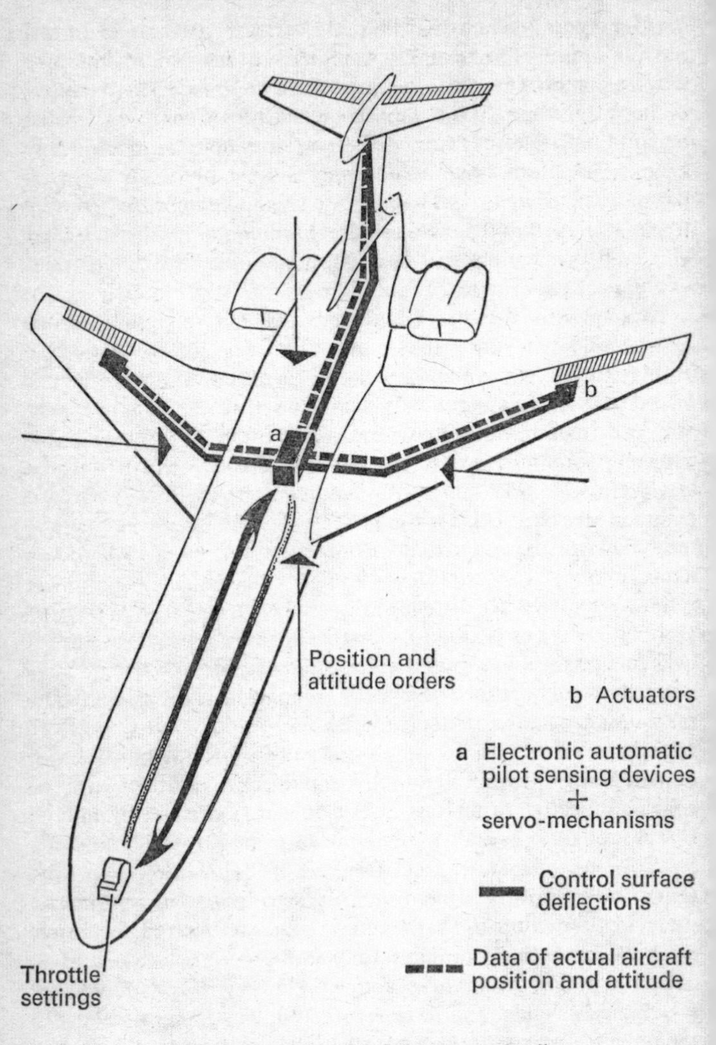


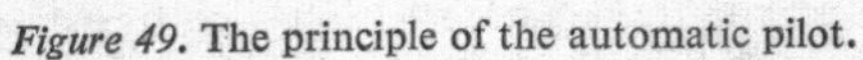
*Figure 49.* The principle of the automatic pilot.

devices so that every cycle of the process scores a bulls-eye on the target. Human beings continue to be used in 'automation' schemes, however, because the technical devices may not be immediately available or convenient, or because workers are cheaper than such devices, or because a deliberate decision has been taken for political and social reasons to retain them, or because managers do not wish to surrender any of their functions to electronic gadgets any more than the rank and file does, or from general inertia or just plain cussedness.

I do not mean to imply that *any* goal for automation can be attained simply because it is formulated. For example I would guess that any attempt to construct a system for the automatic production of 100 different paintings which would be accepted by the Royal Academy would be a waste of time and money. The selection and formulation of the right targets for automation is an essential prerequisite, although it is not sufficient. (But even an impossibly difficult target is better than none at all because the reasons for failure to attain a target can be very instructive.) The selection of the 'right' targets for automation depends on social and economic factors as well as technical, and the power of automation is such that these have to be considered in relation not only to the profit and needs of a particular manufacturer, or of a particular group of consumers, but also to a whole industry or to the whole national economy or, finally, to the needs of the whole population of the world.

To illustrate this, consider the case of the automatic assembly of watches in the Soviet Union. This is one small part of the official Soviet plan to automate the whole of their industrial production, and they seem to be having considerable success. Sir Leon Bagrit points out, in the Reith Lectures already referred to, that on the average the Russians are assembling watches automatically in two-thirds the time normal in Switzerland and three-quarters of the time normal in France. These watches are already available in Europe at lower prices than the Swiss and French products of equivalent quality so that the European watch industry has already been affected. The Russians do not place major emphasis on export of their manufactured goods but should a country such as Japan follow their example and develop an automated watch industry we can be sure that this will force the European firms to automate quickly and large numbers of low-cost watches will appear in the world markets. But who will buy all these watches which will pour out in their millions from automatic plants? No doubt every under-nourished peasant in Asia would be very happy to possess a watch as a free gift and it might be very good politics for the wealthy nations to produce watches for this purpose. But it is obvious that this would transform the whole character and purpose of industrial production in the advanced countries.

The most immediate and the most ominous problem relating to the introduction of automation is that of unemployment. There is general agreement about the material benefits which automation can bring to mankind but there is much disagreement, not to say confusion, as to whether it will create large-scale unemployment. A typical cross-section of hopes and fears was revealed at a conference called 'The Challenge of Automation' held in Duisburg at the beginning of 1965, and attended by over 12,000 businessmen. Dr Louis T. Rader, vice-president and general manager of the General Electric Company's industrial electronics division, told them that American firms had now reached the stage where they had to use automatic industrial processes to compete successfully in home and foreign trade: 'the United States as an industrial economy is automating because we must do so in order to maintain our standard of living and our balance of trade'. American experience during the past decade had shown that there was a relation between automation and economic growth; those firms which adopted automatic processes expanded, made bigger profits, and, contrary to the popular view, created more jobs, said Dr Rader. But Dr Friedrichs, a member of the executive of I.G.Metall, the most powerful trade union in Germany, claimed that between 1958 and 1963 more than a quarter of a million jobs had been lost by workers in Germany through automation. He quoted one firm where, after the new methods had been introduced, only 300 of 800 skilled workers were still needed and the rest were downgraded and lost pay. Herr Sabel, president of the Federal Employment Exchange, denied that growing automation threatened full employment. Herr Berg, president of the Federation of German Industries, said that automation, *per se*, was neither good nor bad and that it was the task of the employers, in collaboration with the workers, to ensure that it was put to good economic and social ends. Professor Mikat, the Minister of Education for North Rhine-Westphalia, said it was clear that automation meant re-education and retraining on a permanent basis.

Haunting all such discussions, whether in Germany, America, Britain or any other capitalist country, is the fear of automation in the minds of the workers who have memories of widespread unemployment and misery due to rationalization measures during the pre-war depression. In spite of the reassurances of many experts, such as Dr Rader, I think these fears are well founded. In Detroit, the birthplace of automation, the same number of cars was produced in 1963 as in 1955 with one-sixth fewer workers. Automation has not created more jobs within the car industry, and viewing the American economy as a whole, it does not appear to have created more jobs overall on balance, since the hard core unemployment in America is as intractable as ever. The general spread of automation, without large-scale planning, could lead to a period of industrial strife and upheaval in the immediate future, compared with which the horrors and miseries of the first industrial revolution will seem like a tea party.

Whatever happens in the short run, in the long run automation will free men from grinding toil, from degrading and dangerous occupations, from repetitive and boring office work. At the same time it will provide all the necessities of a growing world population. If any political system is incompatible with the general adoption of automation, that system will vanish. The big problem of the future which automation will create is: what will men, liberated from the treadmill, the factory, and the counting house, do with their leisure?

## 8

# Electronics and Transport

I travel light; as light,
That is, as a man can travel who will
Still carry his body around because
Of its sentimental value.
Christopher Fry: *The Lady's not for Burning*

ONE of the characteristics of modern life is the extent to which we bustle about from one place to another. Science and technology have given us the means to transport ourselves, our goods and our chattels, to almost any part of our planet – before long, perhaps, to other parts of the solar system – at increasing speeds and in increasing numbers. Whether, on balance, all this travelling to and fro adds to the sum of human happiness and understanding is a moot point – but there can be no doubt about the increase in tempo and amount of travel. It would be interesting to have the figures, if they were available, for the total man-miles covered each year by the world's population, using all forms of transport. The rate of increase of such a yearly total for the twentieth century will surely be getting steeper since it will be compounded by the rapid increase in the world's population and the vastly increased capacity and speed of modern forms of transport. It has been calculated that commuters to urban and industrial centres spend between one-tenth and one-quarter of their waking lives in travelling to and from their places of work. Yet this by no means satisfies their appetite for travel since an increasing number of them take to their cars on days off and join in the rush to go somewhere else. In parallel with all this travel for business and pleasure there is a corresponding increase in the movement of materials and goods, often along the same roads, seaways or air lanes, allocated for the movement of men.

This enormous increase in the density and speed of all forms of traffic demands coordination, forward planning and control on a local, national and international basis but this does not appear to be compatible with sectional and vested interests in transport. Public transport is becoming choked by uncoordinated private transport. If the anarchy is allowed to continue unchecked it cannot be long before it defeats its own object: to transport people and goods safely, quickly and cheaply. In this situation electronics, which is already essential for air transport, is becoming daily more essential for surface transport. More than that, it may offer the only way out of the impasse and eventual chaos into which our transport is now heading.

## AIR TRANSPORT

If any further demonstration of the essential part played by electronics in our lives should be required it could be provided by aviation alone. Every phase of the design, construction, testing, operation and maintenance of aircraft is dependent on electronics. The examples which follow illustrate just a few of the many ways in which this works in practice.

Numerically controlled machine tools, which were described in the chapter on automation, are proving invaluable in the production of aero-engines and aircraft components. For example, the exacting job of providing model die blocks for compressor or turbine blade aerofoils is carried out by Rolls-Royce with a magnetic tape controlled three-dimensional vertical milling machine which can be positioned to two-ten-thousandths of an inch. The computer used to calculate the dimensions of the aerofoils produces the manufacturing tape which instructs the milling machine, eliminating the need for any drawings or templates and the time of highly-skilled toolmakers.

Anyone who has seen the cockpit of a modern airliner will appreciate the formidable problem of displaying flight information to the pilot, who is virtually surrounded by dozens of closely crowded instruments demanding attention. This problem has been intensively studied at the Royal Aircraft Establishment at Farnborough and it now looks as though a satisfactory solution will be found, based on the use of the cathode-ray tube. This can present the most complex forms of display, far surpassing that of any known mechanical systems, and the recent advent of the bright tube, which can be used under any external lighting conditions, removes the only objections to its use.

The great advantages of the electronic system have been

demonstrated with working models by the R.A.E. For example, existing instruments which include airspeed and height information in the basic flight director and altitude display present only a limited sector of the total possible values, because it is not possible to increase the indicated range without overcrowding the display. But by generating number digits electronically any possible indication of height can be shown clearly on a small section of the cathode-ray screen. A typical display of data for altitude, heading, turn, slip, height and airspeed, which would normally require six separate instruments, can be compressed into a few square inches of panel space and would be much easier to read and interpret. Electronic systems of display also make 'time-sharing' possible: that is, a simple programme can be written to select information to be displayed at given stages of a flight so that the same display area can be used several times. Thus information about the undercarriage, which at present occupies permanent space on an over-crowded instrument panel, could be presented on the screen only when it is required at the beginning and end of a flight. Spacesharing, with different displays superposed optically according to the queueing principle could also help to solve the competitive struggle for the pilot's attention which now puts such a strain on him. A variety of presentations made in sequence in the same area can be given on a more generous scale than if they all occupy a fraction of that area permanently.

On 10 June 1965 a British European Airways Trident aircraft, carrying eighty-eight passengers on a scheduled flight from Paris, touched down gracefully at London Airport to make a perfect landing. As the plane taxied to its stand, the chief pilot announced to the passengers over the intercom: 'I have an important announcement to make. This has been different from any previous landing. You are the first people in the world to be landed by an automatic system. This is yet another step towards all-weather landings.' The actual part of the landing which was performed automatically was the 'flare-out', the critical final stage from an altitude of about 50 ft, when the nose starts to come up, until touchdown. It was made possible by an electronic system called 'Autoflare' which had received approval from the Air Registration Board. The system depends on a very accurate and reliable radio

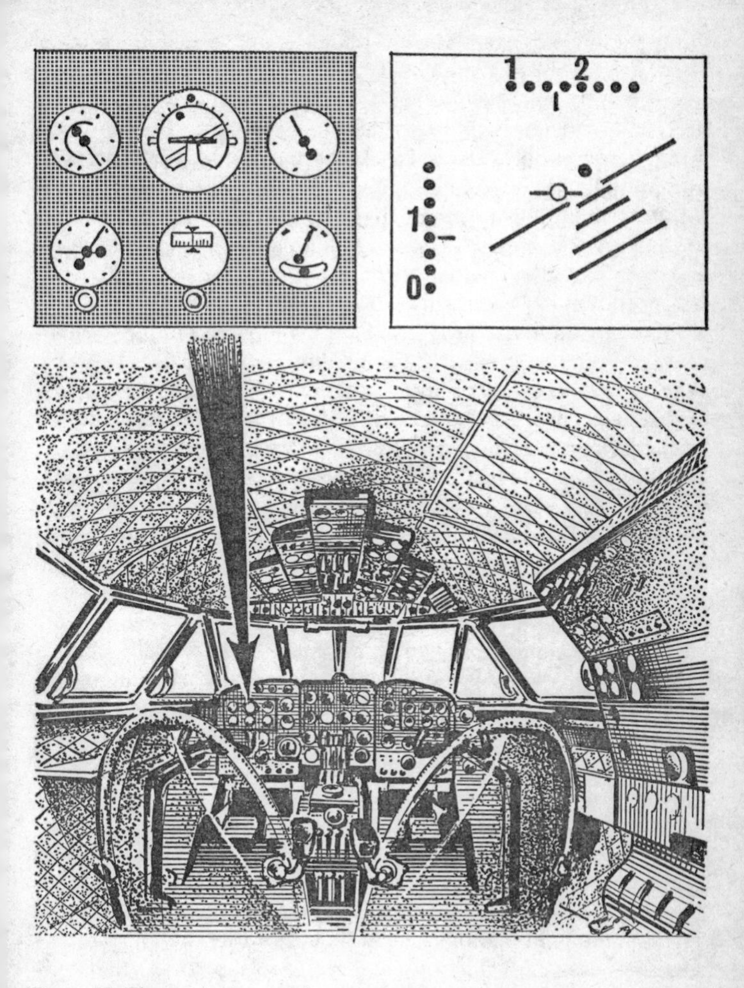


*Figure 50.* Electronics in a modern air-liner. All the information shown on the panel of instruments detailed on the top left of the drawing can be appreciated at a glance on the single electronic display shown on the top right. See page 174. Reproduced by permission of Hawker Siddeley Aviation Ltd.

altimeter made by Standard Telephones which feeds information about the height of the aircraft to a Smith's automatic pilot so that the appropriate path may be followed at the correct rate of descent and the aircraft may touch down in the proper attitude and at the appropriate speed. Before flare-out the pilot steers the aircraft manually in azimuth helped by information derived from localizer aerials at the end of the runway, but it is expected that in three or four years completely automatic 'left-right' steering guidance will also be approved and fully automatic landing, as well as fully automatic flight, will then be available.

Weather conditions may have been the most serious problem in the early days of civil air transport but a much bigger problem now is congestion at airports and even in the air. The way in which electronics is being used to solve this problem is illustrated by two recent developments. The first is a new version of the British Decca Navigator System for short-range navigation, called Harco (hyperbolic area coverage), designed for area coverage and close lateral separation of aircraft on discrete tracks, particularly in regions of high density traffic. The interesting feature in the new system is a small, cheap, light-weight computer called the Decca Omnitrack, which links the radio receiver to a pictorial position display and translates the hyperbolic coordinates of the original system into rectilinear terms. This means that the position of an aircraft in flight can now be inscribed on a conventional chart instead of the distorted projection of the original Decca system. To achieve this the Omnitrack computer performs nineteen multiplications, fourteen additions, one division and one square root every 0·6 second.

The second example of electronic aid to air traffic control is a new automatic aircraft altitude reporting system which is now being tested by the United States Federal Aviation Agency. The airborne equipment in this system includes an aneroid transducer – a device for measuring altitude, similar to the radio altimeter – which sends the altitude signal to an airborne computer for conversion into a code of electronic pulses. When the aircraft is interrogated by a ground-based station its 'transponder' beacon, a device which transmits a coded signal on receipt of a suitable interrogating signal, is triggered off and transmits the coded pulses to the ground installation. The information is displayed on the controller's radar screen: next to the 'blip' (the radar echo of the reporting aircraft) the altitude is shown in hundreds of feet.

Another aspect of the use of electronics in air travel is illustrated by 'PANAMAC', an extensive electronic computer reservations network introduced by Pan American Airways at the beginning of 1965. It consists of two parts: a 'working' section and an information storage section resembling a file cabinet, and it makes use of 165,000 miles of submarine cables, radio circuits and telegraph lines which make up the Pan Am communications network. The network links Pan American offices all over the world with the I.B.M. computer complex in the Pan Am Building in New York. At any of these offices a reservation agent selects a card from a file, inserts it into a slot in his console, depresses keys for the flight number and data desired, and presses a button which asks whether a seat is available. The computer in New York scans the reservation record in a split second: Yes, a seat is available. The message is flashed across oceans and continents to the agent who presses a button marked 'Sell'. The computer in New York then records the reservation and automatically sends a record of the sale back to an electric typewriter which is part of the agent's console. The agent enters the passenger's name, address and telephone number on the typewriter keyboard and this information is sent back immediately to New York to be made part of the passenger's record. A ticket is made out and the number entered on the typewriter, completing the transaction in less time than it has taken to describe it.

With the advances in micro-electronics and the production of extremely reliable circuits described in Chapter 3 it will be possible to introduce entirely automatic control into flying. The various electronic instruments and systems – radar, radio, television – instead of acting as extensions of the senses of pilots, navigators and controllers on the ground, will report to the new computers which will make the decisions. Human judgement will be retained as a desirable redundancy to deal with exceptional situations, but it will be relieved of the strain and fatigue which is now causing serious concern to air-crews and ground control staff. The new very reliable circuits will also make it possible to design aircraft with considerably less built-in aerodynamic stability, and therefore more economically, since the control will be reliable under all conditions.

## SEA TRANSPORT

Electronics, in the form of the early radio transmitters, appeared on ships before it did on aircraft, but the majority of modern electronic equipment now at sea was designed in the first place to meet the more urgent demands of military and civil aircraft and of warships. Since the end of the war, however, a steadily increasing amount of electronic equipment has been designed and developed specifically for shipping. Almost every vessel of any size now carries its marine radar as well as its radio, and both have very much increased the safety of ships at sea and simplified the problems of navigation. Echo-ranging equipment – on the same principle as radar but using sound waves instead of radio waves – is now used to provide information about what lies beneath the surface; trawlers now use it extensively to detect shoals of fish.

The scope of electronics in the merchant marine is illustrated by the recently developed marine data logger, a sort of electronic watchkeeper. One of the most advanced equipments of this kind, designed by English Electric, was installed on a new 8,000-ton refrigerated cargo vessel, the *Zealandic.* It is fitted in the engine room and has its own temperature control system. It watches continuously the operation of 350 points in the ship's main engines, auxiliary machinery, refrigeration equipment and refrigerated cargo space. At each watch change the logger automatically produces a complete record of the condition of each of the 350 points. Immediately anything abnormal occurs the logger raises the alarm, sounds a klaxon, flashes a warning light, and prints out an alarm record with full details of the location of the fault and the time it occurred.

Regarded from the point of view of traffic control, shipping is in general a much less complex problem than air traffic. It is doubtful whether it will ever be worth while to design ships to travel at more than say 100 knots and there are only two dimensions to consider when locating a ship at sea. Against this a ship is usually very much bigger than an aircraft and slower to respond to control operations, and collisions do occur in busy shipping lanes. In the English Channel, one of the most crowded of all sea passages, collisions have become a serious problem and radar is now regarded as essential for all ships using it, not only in fog but also in clear conditions. I have no doubt that before long ships entering such crowded waters will be radar and radio controlled from shore stations as aircraft now are from airports. Dropping the pilot in the future will be a matter of electronics.

## LAND TRANSPORT

Electronic control has not been applied to the various forms of surface transport to the extent that it has in the air, but electronics is already used in many ways for land transport and its importance in this sphere is increasing rapidly. I shall make no attempt to list all the many present and future applications but will select a few examples to illustrate the trends, with particular reference to the motor-car.

The French railway system, one of the most efficient in the world, is already using automatic control of trains, based on electronic techniques, to a considerable and increasing degree. French railways are almost entirely electrified and electronic control is a logical extension of the electric power system.

The New York City Transit Authority has been running a driverless electric train since the beginning of 1962. It operates a shuttle service between Times Square and Grand Central Station, a distance of about half a mile. The speed, braking, acceleration, time of stops, opening and closing of doors, of the train are all carried out entirely automatically according to the instructions on a punched film in the command unit, although a supervisor in Grand Central Station can follow and take over the control at any time.

Automatic control and marshalling of goods wagons is well advanced on many railway systems. British Railways conducted a successful experiment a few years ago in the use of a computer to control its goods wagons in the Cardiff area and found that it was possible to work with eleven per cent fewer wagons. This is likely to lead to a pattern of linked small computers – one for each District – feeding a big central computer in each railway

Region to control the whole of British Railways' rolling stock.

So far, the main application of electronics to motor-cars has been in the major part it plays in automation of car production. In the last few years computer control of this production has been introduced by leading manufacturers in America, France and Britain. In terms of numbers of vehicles produced this has been only too successful, but the prodigious output of these machines in the unplanned economies of the major car-producing countries has had some very undesirable effects with which most of us are only too familiar. All methods of transport based on the use of fossil fuels are bound to become obsolete sooner or later but, since the world's oil reserves will probably suffice for at least another hundred years, it may be some time before the increasing threat of the motor-car to civilized life and well-being is decisively dealt with. Meanwhile, electronics can help us to make the best of a bad job in the shape of extremely efficient road traffic control and automatic control of individual vehicles.

An indication of what can be done with electronic traffic control is the Munich scheme based on the Elliott ARCH Traffic Control computer. This will start with Stachus Square in Munich, reputed to be the busiest traffic centre in Europe. All the roads leading to the square will be controlled by a system depending entirely on the minute to minute traffic situation. The existing Munich scheme is advanced by conventional standards but the computer control system will go far beyond this. The computer will monitor automatically the situation at various points, calculate the signal settings required to obtain optimum traffic flow and make the appropriate adjustments of the traffic lights, all within fractions of a second. It will also count vehicles entering the control area through main or secondary roads and plan ahead to maintain the optimum flow continuously. The computer also stores the tramway timetable for the area and will report periodically to the Munich Tramway Authority on how actual running times compare with the schedule.

Some idea of what can be done in the way of automatic control of cars and lorries is given by a patent recently granted in the United States. This describes an automatic steering system designed to follow a road automatically, without the need for special cables, signals or markings in the road. Once set on a course it can keep the car in the same lane, along the straight and around curves. It relies on an electronic memory. When the driver wants to rest he presses a button and a scanner records a general picture of the scene immediately ahead, including white lines and salient road features. He can then leave the driving to the machine. If the car's relative position starts to change, an electric motor turns the wheel, and if the electronic eye sees an obstacle ahead, such as a slow car, an alarm sounds and the brakes go on. The driver can take over at any time, wipe out the previous memory, and re-record the road image.

## IS THE JOURNEY REALLY NECESSARY?

Travel as an end in itself may constitute one of the main methods of relaxation and education of future society. In the widest sense, which includes travel in outer space and perhaps, in the remote future, beyond the solar system, it will probably constitute one of the most stimulating and significant activities of the human race. We can be sure that however successful extra-terrestrial travel may prove, there is no danger of men or their vehicles overcrowding the vast spaces between the stars. But on the thin skin of this little earth we have already exceeded the optimum traffic density for pleasurable travel by land, sea or air. A great deal can be achieved with modern techniques of control, but congestion on the roads and in the cities is rapidly reaching such proportions that it threatens to get out of any kind of control. As for the air, experts calculate that all the world's major airports will reach saturation within ten years. We must now pay increasing attention to reducing the amount of travel which is *not* pleasurable to a minimum. Sooner or later we shall have to face the question: are all these journeys really necessary? Once again the solution of our problems may be found in the increasing application of electronic techniques, and since this application will have a great effect not only on travel but on the whole of our daily life in the near future, let us consider it in more detail.

The pattern of everyday life for a very large section of the world's urban population – itself a rapidly increasing proportion of the whole population – is largely determined by daily commuting from sprawling suburban zones into overcrowded and densely concentrated business and industrial areas. Until recently one could see little prospect of relief from the increasing congestion and frustration of travelling to work as the pattern began to be repeated in travel for leisure and on holiday. Modern telecommunications and electronic information processing techniques have arrived in time to prevent this modern plague from invading and paralysing the whole of society, and will eventually be the chief means in effecting the cure. The revolution in communications described in Chapter 4 not only produced a huge increase in the number, speed, range and complexity of the messages essential to modern society, but it enabled those messages to be exchanged without the transport of any material bodies or objects whatever. The technology which produced the telegraph, telephone and radio and so increased the efficiency and safety of travel also produced the television receiver and the electronic computer which began to reduce the demand for travel.

The significant changes in home life and leisure brought about by post-war television were the beginnings of a thorough-going revolution in this sphere. Cinema attendances, which had been increasing steadily before the advent of television, began to decline and in less than a decade more Americans and Britons were seeing films through the medium of the television than in the cinemas. Not only cinemas but theatres and sports stadiums found their audiences dwindling as the sales of television sets increased. Some may regret the increasing passivity and lack of participation of audiences who choose electronic entertainment – but was there much active participation by audiences previously? The significant difference in the present context is that the millions who watch at home are not adding to traffic congestion on the roads or overloading the public transport systems.

The existing telephone, radio and television networks are the forerunners of vastly increased personal communications based on the world-wide networks described in Chapter 4, which will be highly developed along similar lines to the electricity power supply networks. In twenty years or so all new houses and building developments will be supplied with comprehensive communication links and outlets as a matter of course, and an increasing number of existing buildings will be linked to the national communication net. Small control consoles for each private house and larger, more complex master controls for flats and public buildings, will provide all necessary switching and connexions to the network of the communication equipment on individual sites. This equipment will include television cameras and display screens, microphones and loudspeakers, storage and recording equipment, security and privacy circuits. The choice of a score or more of national and international television and radio programmes catering for all needs and tastes will be selected by push button or voice-operated controls.

The present facilities provided by the telephone systems will be extended in many ways: in addition to automatic connexion to more than two hundred million subscribers all over the world, the provision of an increasing number of videophones will enable users to see as well as hear one another. Information about weather, current events, public services will be presented visually as well as audibly. Computer controlled libraries of recorded music, films, plays, operas, books, paintings, etc., would allow the individual subscriber to reproduce any selected item from the whole range of the arts on the relatively simple reproducing equipment in his living-room. For those who want it, facsimile and electronic printing and storage equipment will enable any of the material transmitted over the lines to be 'frozen' for as long as may be required. No doubt many subscribers will not aspire to any greater heights than news summaries complete with pictures on their breakfast tables, or printed lists of the afternoon racing results taken straight from the video. But the same techniques will allow us to read a page from *Paradise Lost* at leisure or visit an art gallery without moving from our armchairs.

Whatever else all this is leading to – whether you regard it as desirable or not – it will undoubtedly reduce drastically the travelling involved in the enjoyment of the things described as well as the physical transport of goods and persons previously required to present them. The implications go a good deal beyond this. Looking a little farther into the future, when the great majority of the world's population will have an individual 'telecom number', we can see a comprehensive two-way link between person to person and individual to communications centre. People will not only be able to refer to a continuously up-dated summary of knowledge on any subject but will also be able to ask questions and receive considered replies. Programmed learning will then be within the reach of all – and if we insist that human teachers are essential then human teachers can be integrated into the system. Although many kinds of skill and learning depend on physical contact with things, large parts of the learning process consist essentially of communication and interchange of ideas. Many schoolchildren who have spent fruitless hours creeping like snails to crowded schools will continue their education in adult life in the comfort of their own homes.

The development of automation in business and industry allied to the new communications, will also prove a powerful force for getting rid of the existing wasteful and unpleasant commuting system, in which harassed travellers hardly have time to recover from the ordeal of getting to work before they must face the prospect of struggling home again. The organization and size of future towns will depend on many factors but I think there is a good case to be made out for limiting the size of towns so that they do not serve a population of more than about 200,000. The conversion of our present unwieldy cities into self-contained units of this size will obviously be a long and perhaps a painful process but I think it must come eventually. If it were achieved it would be possible for each member of the community to be linked by television as well as telephone with all the others. Once the communication net is in full operation a large proportion of the physical transport of goods as well as bodies would become redundant. The development of the computer has already accelerated the trend by automatic processing of the complex data needed for the control of modern industrial production, business and office administration, warehousing, merchandizing, etc., and transmitting the raw and processed data between one building and another, between office and factory in the same town, between different towns in the same country and between businesses in different countries separated by hundreds or thousands of miles.

Businessmen now go to extraordinary pains and expense to travel across oceans and continents, often for a few minutes' conversation with other businessmen. When supersonic aircraft are in service it will be possible to reach the Antipodes in seven hours. But with the aid of a world communication network they can be reached with far less trouble and expense in a few seconds.

Conferences will take place between delegates from all parts of the world with less inconvenience and time lost in travelling than if they were all in the same town.

Although this end may not be pursued consciously it is evident that one of the major effects of the technological revolution will be to reduce drastically the huge volume of routine travel to which we have now grown accustomed and which is now the despair of town planners and governments. When the social revolution which follows begins to take effect, travel for pleasure will once again be a pleasurable occupation. Unhurried and relaxed travellers may once more experience the chief delight of travelling – that of dallying on the way.

# 9
# Electronics and War

War is much too serious a thing to be left to military men. — Talleyrand

THERE is no clear division between the technology of peace and the technology of war – the important difference lies in the application. Electronics, the key technology of our time, has revolutionized the business of war no less than the pursuits of peace. The important discoveries in electronics, described in earlier chapters, were made in times of peace but the rapid development of the electronic industry between 1940 and 1950 was due to the urgent demands of war. The fact that today something like seventy-five per cent of the huge electronics industry in the United States is directed to military applications does not indicate, as some people imagine, that there is some sort of fundamental affinity between electronics and war. It is simply that the American Government has decided to use it for war – or rather, since no government admits that it has any intention to make war, for defence. In the much smaller British electronics industry military applications now account for about twenty per cent of the total but it could be turned over rapidly to full-scale war production if the need arose. This orientation of electronics towards military uses, which is common to all the major powers, shows the importance of its role in modern warfare. Some aspects of this will be discussed in this chapter.

## GUIDED WEAPONS

In the present phase of their political and military alignment it is clear that neither of the two major nuclear powers has resorted to the use of nuclear weapons because each fears retaliation by the other. The maintenance of this balance of terror depends on the ability of either side to launch, direct and deliver on specified targets enough nuclear bombs to inflict catastrophic casualties and damage, *whatever the other side does first*. Professor Dennis

Gabor points out in his book *Inventing the Future* that the virtual certainty of the 'dead man's revenge' depends on the fact that both the U.S.A. and the U.S.S.R. are very large countries even compared with the area of destruction of multi-megaton bombs, and that each has solid-fuel rockets in instant readiness distributed over widely dispersed bases. But equally these deadly weapons must be launched from their fixed or mobile bases automatically and guided automatically to their targets in any circumstances, and this depends on electronics.

The Germans began the development of guided weapons as early as 1933. Had their electronics been as advanced as that of the Allies, and had they possessed atomic warheads, the course of the war and its outcome would have been very different. Even the relatively crude V1 and V2 weapons – the 'secret weapons' which Hitler hoped would win the war for him – were a very serious threat and the need to eliminate or overrun their launching pads was treated as a primary strategic objective. By the end of the war the Germans had developed a whole family of guided missiles, including some with television eyes and radio control, though not all had reached the production stage. The Allied powers took over the development of guided weapons at the end of the hot war and each pursued it independently during the cold war which followed. The work was kept secret (except, of course, from the experts and professionals on either side whose business it was to know what the others were up to) so that it was not generally known that no expense was spared and a high proportion of the technical and scientific man-power of America, Russia and Britain was devoted to the complex problems which had to be solved. Not the least of these problems was how to overcome the obstruction of influential military men who were just as suspicious of the application of electronics and automation to war as many industrialists were of their application to industry.

Modern guided weapons form only one element in a complex defence system, based on the most advanced electronic techniques. It includes distant early warning radar screens, radar interrogation, an outer ring of bases for interceptor fighters with air-to-air missiles, an inner ring of radar for surface-to-air anti-missile missiles, and finally the inter-continental ballistic missiles themselves in hardened bases or beneath the sea in nuclear submarines.

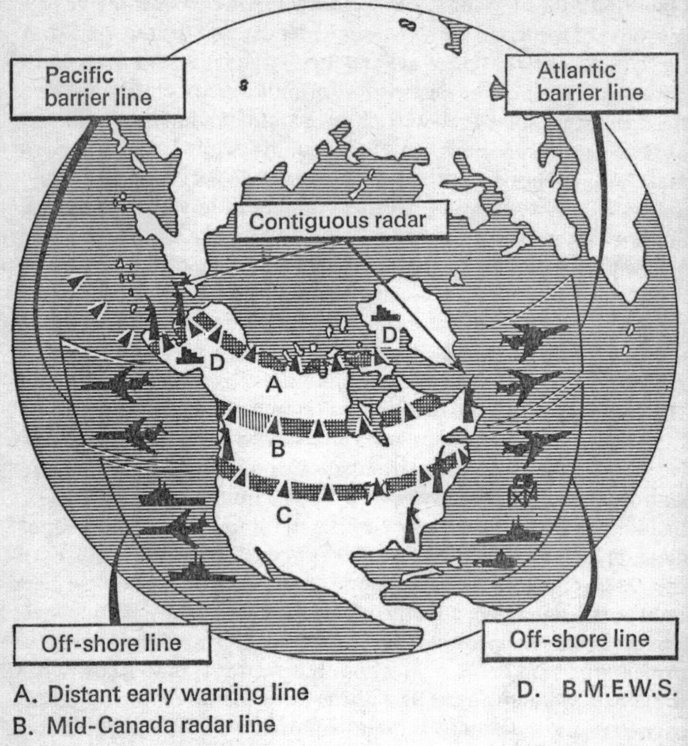


*Figure 51.* The system for the defence of the North American continent depends on extensive radar installations. See pages 188, 189.

According to the information released the chain of radar lines forming the elaborate defence system for the North American continent was completed at the beginning of 1961. The most northerly of the lines is the Distant Early Warning Line (DEW), across the extreme northern rim of the continent. This operates in conjunction with the Ballistic Missile Early Warning System (BMEWS) with stations in Alaska, Greenland and Yorkshire. The BMEWS alone is reported to have cost one billion dollars. Six hundred miles south of the DEW line, is the Mid-Canada Line forming an arc across the middle of the Canadian continent. About the same distance farther south is the Pinetree arc of radars across the whole of southern Canada, supported by a 'contiguous' radar system in the United States and operated jointly by the U.S.A. and Canada. In the United States itself the system is supported by ships and aircraft equipped with radar and stationed in the Atlantic and the Pacific. In the Atlantic there are a number of Texan Tower radar stations, each sixty to eighty miles offshore, which can instantly transmit warnings of air attack to the headquarters of North American Air Defence Command at Colorado Springs. The system is designed not to ensure interception and destruction of all enemy missiles before they reach their targets – an impossibly difficult objective – but to give adequate warning of their approach so that instant retaliation is certain. The Russians have a corresponding system over the vast territories of the U.S.S.R. I think it is fairly safe to assume that the Intelligence Organizations of both powers are well acquainted with the details of both systems.

The control and guidance of the missiles themselves depends on the whole range of electronic techniques and components. There are a number of categories of guided weapons which include: air-to-air, surface-to-air, underwater-to-surface (e.g. Polaris) and surface-to-surface (e.g. ICBMS). Their guidance systems differ according to the nature of the missile but in all cases two distinct technical problems have to be solved: the control of the attitude of the missile, that is its orientation in space; and the control of the path of the missile, so that it reaches its target. The first problem is generally solved during the launching phase so that the missile is set on its correct path. The path control depends primarily on whether the target is moving or stationary, but there are generally two phases of guidance: mid-course and terminal guidance. The function of mid-course guidance is to carry the missile's warhead as close as possible to the target in the shortest possible time. Finally in the terminal guidance stage the warhead must be brought to within killing distance of the target and exploded.

A surface-to-air missile, aimed for instance at fast-moving aircraft, may be launched on a radar beam into the correct flight path, guided by a command guidance system to its target, and homed on its target by some kind of homing device. Command guidance from the ground may use one radar for tracking the target and another for tracking the missile, as well as a command radio. The information from the two radars is fed into a computer on the ground which rapidly calculates the correct path for the missile and issues the necessary instructions to the command radio to direct the missile. At short range a homing device in the missile takes over for the kill; it may send out its own radar pulses, or sense the radiation from the target, or use a number of other methods which are closely guarded secrets. This brief description of automatic interception is considerably simplified; in practice the problem is much more complex. The aircraft will take evasive action and instead of heading directly towards the target the missile has to anticipate where the target is going to be when the missile arrives at it. There are also ways in which the radar pulses and command signals may be jammed or confused and further ways in which this can be avoided – electronics has transformed the 'battle' into a battle of wits between the scientists and electronic engineers of both sides.

In the case of the long-range surface-to-surface missile – the ICBM – all the electronic equipment is included (and expended) in the missile itself. To ensure that a large multi-stage rocket vehicle carrying a hydrogen bomb in its warhead can be detonated within a radius of a few miles of a target 5,000 miles away requires a great deal of intricate and expensive control equipment. A computer is built into the missile to deal with the many unpredictable factors which can affect its flight: such as variations in temperature and density of the upper atmosphere, air currents and gusts of wind, variations in the performance of the power plant, malfunctioning of the control surfaces, etc. The navigation systems are marvels of precision engineering. One declassified system is called inertial guidance, and has the advantage that it cannot be affected by outside interference or give any warning of its approach. It is based on three very sensitive accelerometers which accurately detect accelerations in three dimensions and are coupled to three gyroscopes which provide a three-dimensional frame of reference for the missile. In this way, the distance travelled from the launching pad, in each dimension, can be calculated. During flight the computer receives data from the navigation and sensing devices, and if these differ from those stored in its memory, automatic corrections are made immediately. Accuracy of flight is doubly ensured by automatic checking of the precise position of the missile in space using star-tracking devices, or measurements of the earth's magnetic field or a radio grid system transmitted over the route.

The ICBM poses a very difficult problem for the defence. Modern radar systems are capable of detecting the approach of long-range missiles at considerable distances, but to detect them is one thing and to destroy them at a safe distance is another. Both the Americans and the Russians claim that they have effective anti-missile missiles but nothing short of 100 per cent interception of all the attacking missiles at long range is good enough when those missiles contain hydrogen bombs, and this certainly cannot be achieved now. Until it can be, the only defence is the certainty of immediate retaliation, as described above. Electronics, which has made push-button warfare possible, also makes it possible to reply to an attack when no finger is available to push the button.

## AUTOMATIC WARSHIPS

The amount of electronic equipment used on warships has increased steadily since 1940. A modern aircraft-carrier may have more than £5 million worth of electronic equipment. Nearly half the total cost of the latest American nuclear submarine is accounted for by the electronic systems. The conditions of modern war impose the necessity on battleships of dealing with a vast amount of information very quickly and acting on it quickly. All this information is collected by electronic equipment, including radio, radar and sonar equipment; it is processed by computers; the processed information is translated into the necessary action by the ship and its armament. Until recently the introduction of all this electronic equipment did not lead to a reduction in the ship's manpower. On the contrary there was an additional requirement for highly skilled maintenance men. But this is now changing. The new electronic equipment has become much more reliable and much more automatic.

H.M.S. *Eagle*, a carrier in the Royal Navy which was re-commissioned in 1964 after a major refit, illustrates the trend towards the automatic warship. The whole of the 'action data automation' (ADA) for the *Eagle* is provided by the £1 million Poseidon digital computer developed jointly by the Admiralty Surface Weapons Research Establishment and the electronic firms Ferranti, Mullard and Pye. This giant computer, which can perform half a million additions a second with not more than one error after 16 million additions, is designed to process automatically at great speed the flood of information which pours into it from the ship's radars. It solves the complex problems of interception of aircraft by missiles and recommends the necessary actions to be taken for maximum effect against the enemy. The Poseidon replaces sixty sailors and does their jobs with a speed and efficiency which they could never attain. It is quite capable of taking over many of the other control operations on the ship, for instance, control of the engine room.

Use of the integrated circuits and molecular electronics described in Chapter 3 will meet all the stringent requirements for equipment on modern warships. This must occupy the minimum amount of space, yet continue to operate reliably after being subjected to vibration, shock, extremes of temperature and salt water. When these microelectronic techniques have been fully developed the fully automatic warship will become possible. It will then be the equivalent of an automatically defended mobile surface platform for the launching of guided missiles, and the limited number of men on board will be mostly highly trained electronics experts. To become ruler of the Queen's Navy then it will not be sufficient to polish up the handles on a big front door – aspiring admirals will have to polish up their electronics.

## THE DEATH RAY MYTH

It is a sad reflection on our times that no sooner does a new scientific discovery emerge from the laboratory than there is speculation about its military possibilities. This applies in particular to discoveries in electronics which have been the hunting ground of military-sponsored research for the last twenty years. When the laser was invented (see Chapter 4) and it was demonstrated that a laser beam, suitably focused by a lens, could puncture a steel plate or vaporize a diamond in its path, it was ailed in some quarters as the long-awaited 'Death Ray'. There 'as much speculation, which was not confined to the sensational ress, about the possibility of using an intense laser beam to estroy missiles in flight. It was even suggested that bases could e set up on the moon from which lethal laser beams could be irected to burn up targets on earth.

But however important it may seem to some men to find ever nore efficient ways of destroying others, they cannot alter the ws of nature. Professor Hans Thirring (in the *New Scientist*, Jo. 343, June 1963) has pointed out what nonsense these naginary applications of a laser turn out to be when they are xamined scientifically. Taking the suggestion of using a laser eam to destroy a missile in flight, he points out that the beam onsists of microwaves or light waves which cannot penetrate natter in the way which the much more penetrating X-rays and amma rays do. The only way in which they could pierce the nantle of a bomb would be by melting it. It is true, as described n Chapter 4, that the extraordinary degree of concentration of ne laser beam makes it possible to focus all its energy into a very nall area, and that *over this very small area* it will, in sufficient me, melt substances in its path. But the missile does not bligingly carry a lens to focus the laser beam so that the nly way to destroy it is to hit the whole surface of the missile 'ith enough energy and for a long enough time to melt the overing.

Professor Thirring shows that using a low estimate for the 'eight of the bomb casing of 100 lb., the energy required to melt nis amount of steel in 1 min. is more than 800 kilowatts. If ne missile is 50 kilometres away the cross-sectional area of the eam at that point will be at least 200 times the area of the nissile so that the total energy which would have to be pumped nto the beam to ensure destruction would have to be more than 00 × 800 kilowatts or more than 160 megawatts. This is more nan a billion times the energy which can be put into a laser beam far. Even if it ever became possible to pour this tremendous mount of power into one laser beam there would still remain ne fantastically difficult problems of throwing this extremely arrow beam through the earth's atmosphere to hit a distant st-moving small object and maintaining it on that object for at

least one minute. As for death-ray bases on the moon, Professo
Thirring shows that even if we were able to install a 1,000 mega
watt laser on the moon (about ten billion times what has so fa
been achieved on earth) the maximum intensity of the radiatio
which could be produced with it at any spot on earth would b
less than one-tenth of the intensity of solar radiation in th
temperate zones.

There is one possible military application of the laser describe
by Professor Thirring, which makes use of the fact that there i
one target which provides its own lens to concentrate the lase
beam – the human eye. There have been cases reported of damag
to the retina of the eye where a research worker has looke
directly into the laser beam and no doubt laser weapons could b
made to produce temporary or permanent blindness at lon
range. This is a peculiarly repellent notion but perhaps not mor
so than the use of napalm on human targets.

## ELECTRONIC ESPIONAGE

Electronics plays a very big part in the unsavoury world o
espionage – in real life as well as in popular fiction. Not the leas
disconcerting aspect of this world is that, however unlikely th
exploits of some incredible super-spy of fiction, something eve
more unlikely may turn up in deadly earnest in real life 'scientific
spying.

What, for instance, is one to make of a remarkable applicatio
for lasers discussed in a Senate judiciary sub-committee hearin
held in Washington not long ago, and reported in the Londo
*Times* of 19 January 1965? The hearing was concerned with th
art of electronic surveillance and its possible use for 'unwarranted
invasions of privacy (agencies such as Military Intelligence, th
Central Intelligence Agency, the Federal Bureau of Investigation
and agencies for industrial, labour, state, local law enforcemen
or private-eye spying were specifically excluded from the investi
gation, so presumably invasions of privacy by these organization
were not to be challenged) and one of the expert witnesses,
retired employee of Bell Laboratories, demonstrated a laser. H
said that engineers were working on a modulation device whic
would enable its concentrated beam of light to be aimed at a roon

hundreds of yards away so that it would reflect back a television picture of everything happening in that room.

If such a device is perfected it will go a long way towards destroying the little privacy we can now enjoy. It is fairly common knowledge by now that anyone using a telephone, or, indeed anyone in the proximity of a telephone handset, can be 'bugged' by cheap and efficient electronic devices which are very difficult to detect and automatically record all conversations in a room on a remotely controlled tape recorder. Much effort and misplaced ingenuity has gone into the perfection of these and similar devices, such as: microphones which can be concealed in a packet of cigarettes, the clasp of a tie or the olive of a Martini; midget transmitter-receivers or tape-recorders which can be worn on a holster under the arm. These gadgets are not now restricted to professional snoopers or illusionists but can be bought over or under the counter by anyone bent on a bit of amateur spying.

Hardly a single development in modern science and technology has been neglected by the espionage organizations of the wealthier governments in their elaborate spy games, and in this field, as in the others we have reviewed, electronics plays the dominant role. Computers, radars, lie-detectors, midget transmitters, television cameras, are all used lavishly by organizations such as the Central Intelligence Agency which employs 15,000 persons and spends about £166 million a year to gather information from friends and foes the world over. Artificial satellites, packed with the most sophisticated electronic equipment, can count the ICBMs on the launching pads in Soviet Kazakhstan, follow the count-down of a sputnik launching, or monitor the conversations between Moscow and a Soviet submarine in Pacific waters. The Russians, as we know, have their own satellites.

Therefore, before dismissing the laser which can see through walls as too unlikely in the present state of the art, let us not forget that some of the snooping tools described above would have been regarded as equally fantastic ten years ago. It is now reliably reported (*The Times* 27 April 1966) that the C.I.A., not content with the ability to convert the whole telephone or electric wiring system of a building into listening devices for any conversations within, are developing a highly sensitive device which will pick up from afar conversation between speakers in a closed room, by recording the window vibrations caused by the speakers' voices. It is interesting to speculate on the possible answers to this by counter-espionage: portable sound-proof enclosures? a compact acoustic jammer? or simply intensive training courses for all spies in deaf and dumb show?

Whether governments could get better value for money than by spending it on spies and their equipment would, I think, be worth discussing. In spite of all the expensive props and highly paid agents, the spy game often descends to the level of pure farce. There is one famous example of what I might call Parkinson's Law of Espionage: the more complex the technical equipment used for spying the less the spies have to show for it. It starts one day in 1960 when an agent of the C.I.A. boarded a plane in Tokyo, flew to Singapore, and booked into a hotel room there in time to receive a visitor. The agent plugged a lie-detector into a mains socket, overloaded the circuit, blew the fuses and plunged the building into darkness. An investigation followed and the C.I.A. agent and a colleague were arrested and gaoled as American spies. The affair grew into an international incident which is still having its repercussions on the C.I.A. Ultimately, it led the United States Government to tell a lie in public and then to admit the lie to an even bigger public. Infuriated and humiliated American citizens have been asking questions about the C.I.A. ever since.

Weighing up all this I am inclined to remain sceptical about the laser which will see through walls. This lays me open to the accusation of being a hopeless stick-in-the-mud, but at the moment I really cannot see how the device can be made effective against the normal precautions of citizens protecting themselves from the attentions of Peeping Toms – namely, drawing the curtains and plugging the keyhole. But I have no doubt that some highly paid experts are working on it now.

## 10

# Electronics and the Life Sciences

> Electronics is destined to play a humanitarian role of major significance.
>
> Dr Vladimir K. Zworykin

As with every other branch of human knowledge and social activity to which it has been applied, electronics has proved a potent tool for the life sciences. With its aid revolutionary advances have been made in research into the nature of life, in the measurement and study of living processes, and in all the main fields of medicine. These advances are less familiar, perhaps than those in the industrial and military fields, but as they are at least as important I shall outline some of them in this chapter and touch on some of the very exciting future possibilities.

### ELECTRONIC INSTRUMENTS FOR BIOLOGY AND MEDICINE

The optical microscope was the basis of our knowledge of the organization and structure of individual living cells for nearly three hundred years but many very small structures connected with living things – the filterable viruses for example – remained beyond the range of even the most powerful optical microscope and were never seen until the invention of the electron microscope. Readers who remember that electrons can behave like very short waves as well as like very small particles, will have no difficulty in understanding the principle of the electron microscope. It corresponds in many ways to an optical microscope with the light waves replaced by electron waves and glass lenses replaced by electron lenses. The latter may consist of coils of wire carrying currents to create defined magnetic fields, or metal plates charged to high voltages to create defined electrostatic fields, but in either case the electron beam is bent as the light beam is bent in a light microscope. In addition to the lens system there must be an electron gun to provide a high velocity stream of electrons, and a fluorescent screen or stage on which the magnified electron image is projected. In addition, the necessity to ensure a high vacuum in the instrument as well as various high-voltage stabilized power supplies usually means that the electron microscope is a large, complex and expensive instrument, but its value to research is commensurate.

To examine an object in an electron microscope extremely thin sections of it are placed in the evacuated enclosure where they are

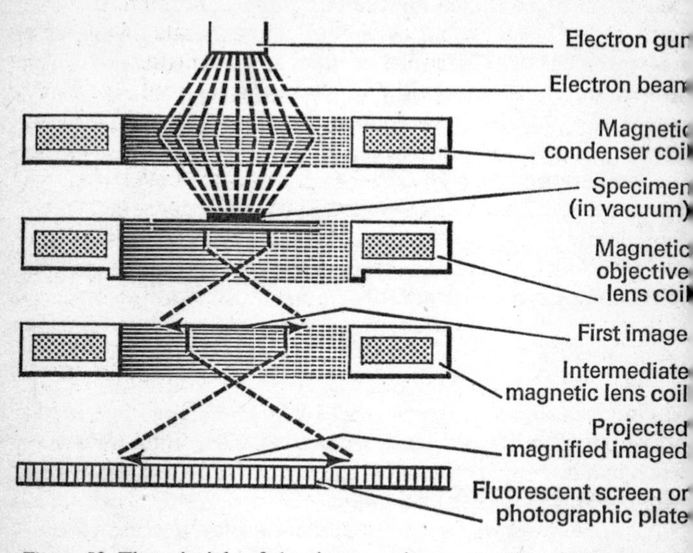


*Figure 52.* The principle of the electron microscope using electromagnetic lenses.

traversed by the electron beam from the gun. In much the same way as a film transparency produces an optical image in a projector, the object produces an electron image according to the manner in which its different parts stop more or fewer electrons, and this image is focused and magnified by the lens system and projected on to the viewing screen, or on to a photographic plate if photomicrographs are required. The higher the speed of the electrons from the gun the shorter the effective wavelength of the electron beam, and with the latest high-voltage instruments the electrons are accelerated to speeds where their equivalent wavelength is only about one hundred-thousandth of the wavelength of ordinary light. With a light microscope details separated by one wavelength of ordinary light – about 20 millionths of an inch – can just be distinguished. The theoretical resolution possible with an electron microscope is therefore a hundred-thousandth of this – less than a billionth of an inch. In practice, nothing like this can be obtained because of imperfections in the lenses and the extreme difficulty of cutting and mounting sufficiently thin sections, but even in the present state of the art an improvement of at least one order of magnitude better than the resolution of the best optical microscope is achieved, and objects separated by one- or two-millionths of an inch can be distinguished. Using one of the new highly ingenious and extremely precise ultramicrotomes, sections only two-millionths of an inch thick prepared from cell tissues have made it possible to reveal structures in the electron microscope which were invisible in ordinary microscopes. For example, the cytoplasm, the jelly-like substance which fills the interior of plant and animal cells, reveals little or no structure in an ordinary high power microscope but an electron microscope reveals a network of minute channels communicating with the cell wall, and these are now known to play an important part in the life of the cell.

Although much has been learned about the fine structure of living cells with the electron microscope it is not possible to observe these details without interfering drastically with the normal equilibrium of the cells, since they have to be sectioned, mounted, placed in a vacuum, and exposed to electron bombardment. A new instrument, which could be described as a radio microscope, has recently been developed at the Western Reserve University in Cleveland, Ohio, to examine living molecules without disturbing them. When we wish to learn what the atoms in any organism are doing we normally make contact with the atoms' outer shells of electrons by using light, electricity or chemicals. But since these outermost electrons are already involved in the electrical and chemical processes of life itself we inevitably alter or even totally destroy the processes and systems in the act of getting information from them. The new instrument, based on what is called nuclear magnetic resonance (NMR), emits radio waves which travel through the outer electron shells of the atoms without disturbing them but which have an effect on the nucleus. Many atomic nuclei have a characteristic spin and precession in a steady magnetic field, the rate of precession being a characteristic of each type of nucleus. A radio signal in tune with the precession of a given nucleus can induce all the nuclei of that type to precess, and as they do so they emit a characteristic radio signal of their own which can be detected. The precession of the nuclei creates a kind of 'friction' which steadily reduces the amount of precession and this causes a gradual fading of the corresponding radio signal.

The technique with the radio microscope is as follows. The animal being studied is supported between the poles of a powerful magnet, while radio signals are transmitted to the animal and the return signals carefully recorded. If the transmitter and receiver are properly in tune, a great variety of chemical species can be detected and their motions and immediate environments described in considerable detail. During an early test with the new instrument on living frog muscle it was tuned to the frequency of hydrogen, an element which is always abundant in living tissue. It was found that the return signal due to the hydrogen NMR faded more slowly when the muscle was contracting than when it was relaxed. It is suggested that water in the muscle is attached to the protein molecules in much the same way as water molecules are held in ice crystals, and when the muscle contracts the water molecules are apparently set free to wander like normal molecules of a liquid.

Another electronic instrument which has overcome great difficulties in the observation of living cells is the ultra-violet colour-translating television microscope. Most cells appear almost entirely transparent in visible microscopy and it is extremely difficult to obtain adequate information about the distribution and concentration of the cell components using ordinary light. Since in many cells these components show much more characteristic differences in absorption of ultra-violet light the use of ultra-violet microscopes was a big advance. However they can be used only with stationary objects which must be exposed to lethal doses of ultra-violet radiation. Further, to determine the concentrations of the various components of the cell it is necessary to expose the specimen to a sequence of illuminations of different wavelengths in the ultra-violet range and this is a long and tedious process.

The ultra-violet colour television microscope, which we owe largely to the post-war work of Dr Zworykin, the inventor of the iconoscope, gives an almost immediate insight into the quantitative distribution of the chemical components in the living, moving, cell. With this instrument, magnified red, blue and green images are thrown in rapid succession on the screen of a colour television set. These are produced by an ultra-violet image convertor, the three coloured images corresponding to three selected wavelengths of ultra-violet radiation. The use of an ultra-violet vidicon (see Chapter 5) permits low-intensity radiation so that the cell is not damaged. On the TV screen the three coloured images are fused by persistence of vision into a single multi-coloured image whose colours reveal at a glance the ultra-violet absorption characteristics of the different chemical components in the specimen. Many rapid changes in the living cell which could not be detected with any other instrument can now be observed and recorded on cine-film.

The behaviour and characteristics of individual cells form one aspect of living things which is giving up its secrets to electronic instruments. Another equally important aspect is the coordinated interaction of millions of such cells which achieves the functions of living organs and animals, and here again electronics has provided us with superb methods of investigation. The activities of living cells are invariably accompanied by electrical signals or associated phenomena which are readily converted into electrical form by suitable transducers. The currents involved may be extremely small and a special class of amplifiers has been developed to amplify them so that they are large enough to be conveniently recorded. A characteristic pattern for many of the instruments used in biology and medicine is therefore: a probe to pick up the signal or a transducer to convert the changes into electric currents, followed by a biological amplifier to amplify the signal faithfully, and finally some form of recorder. The best-known examples of this class of instruments are the electrocardiograph and the electroencephalograph. The electrocardiograph is now regarded as an indispensable aid in the diagnosis and treatment of heart disease. Modern battery operated versions of these instruments, using transistors in place of valves, are completely portable and independent of external power supplies so that the physician needs to carry nothing bigger than a suitcase to obtain accurate and reliable electrocardiograms under any circumstances. The electroencephalograph produces visible records of the complex activity of the human brain and has proved invaluable not only in detecting abnormalities of brain function but also in the study of the behaviour of normal brains.

Brain waves and heart throbs produce electric currents which can be detected and interpreted by attaching suitable electrodes to the surface of the body and connecting these by wires to instruments of the type described above. But it is often required to measure or record the functions of internal organs which are not manifested at the surface, and it may be important to carry out these measurements while the body is walking or running about so that wire connexions are not practicable. Miniaturization has made it possible to design electronic probes and transducers which can be introduced into almost any part of the body without interfering materially with its function, and which will transmit data to receivers outside the body. Such devices are called (somewhat sonorously) endoradiosondes by analogy with the radiosondes used in meteorology. A variety of endoradiosondes can be used to monitor bodily functions such as temperature, pressure, blood flow, digestion, ventilation, etc. The radio pill is a good example. This is a miniature broadcasting station, measuring less than a tenth of a cubic inch, which is easily swallowed or inserted into any of the body cavities without discomfort to the subject. For investigation of the alimentary tract the radio pill is simply taken by mouth and sends out the information collected by its transducers in the form of a modulated radio signal which is received in the normal way. Electronic apparatus has also been developed for the automatic tracking of the pill during its passage through the body so that the telemetered data can be correlated with its precise position in the alimentary canal and this has produced much new knowledge about the digestive system.

Information about objects and structures inside the living body can also be obtained with the use of ultrasonic techniques. The instruments work essentially on the radar principle but the pulses which they send out are not electromagnetic waves but very high-frequency sound waves. These pulses, generated by piezo-electric crystals, can be used to produce an 'echo' picture of the interior of the body on the screen of a cathode-ray tube in a similar way to the charting of submarines beneath the sea by Asdic or Sonar equipment in surface vessels. The technique has been particularly successful in examination of the living brain inside the intact skull, and, since it is fast and harmless and can be used during an operation or by the bedside, may replace the use of X-rays for this purpose.

## COMPUTER APPLICATIONS

Both analogue and digital computers have opened up new areas in biological and medical research although their full impact has yet to be felt. Many biological systems are extremely complex and defy analysis with conventional methods but analogue computers can be used to set up electrical models of these systems which provide a complete analysis. Analogue computers have been used to simulate the action of the heart and blood vessels, the liver, the kidneys and other organs and have led to a much better understanding of how these work. Another method of approach in studying biological phenomena is to invent some theories about their mechanism, write the corresponding differential equations, and see if the experimental data agree with the solutions of these equations. If not, a new set of equations is written and tried in turn, and so on. The solution of equations of this kind can be extremely difficult and tedious, or even impossible by conventional methods, but they can usually be solved numerically with digital computers.

Digital computers are also used to deal with the vast amount of information which is obtained in the course of biochemical and biological investigation. An outstanding example was the collection and interpretation of a large number of X-ray pictures of the haemoglobin and myoglobin molecules by Dr M. Perutz and Dr J. C. Kendrew, which enabled them to construct models of the molecules and make a tremendous step forward in unravelling the nature of the protein molecule, the basic chemical unit of living matter. They were awarded the Nobel Prize for this work which would have been immensely more difficult without the aid of a digital computer.

Digital computers have been used successfully in both the

U.S.A. and the U.S.S.R. to assist doctors in making a rapid diagnosis of disease. The patient's symptoms are fed into the computer which is programmed to compare them with a large number of possible combinations of symptoms stored in its memory. It rapidly prints out a list of the possible conditions which might give rise to the particular group of symptoms and the doctor has to decide between just a few diseases instead of having to consider a large number which he might have thought possible. A logical extension of this technique is to fit suitable monitors, of the type already described, to the patient so that data relating to his condition are relayed either by line or by telemetry to be processed by the computer. This is substantially what is done now in measuring the physiological reactions of astronauts circling the earth and there is no technical reason why it should not become an integral part of a national health service.

The setting up of a computer national health network to collect and store all medical records and vital statistics would represent a major advance in preventive medicine as well as in the diagnosis of disease, since both the normal and the abnormal for any group or individual could be accurately and rapidly established. The very limited use which has been made of computers for this purpose has paid off very handsomely and the delay in the introduction of a comprehensive system is mainly due to shortage of funds. When any government decides that a computer network for this purpose is worth the cost of an aircraft carrier a great step forward in public health will be made.

## THE ELECTRONIC NURSE

One of the many ways in which electronics can be enlisted by the medical services is by using the electronic nurse. When this is installed in a hospital, one nurse can supervise hundreds of patients from a central control panel. Each patient is fitted with light-weight transducers, fixed by sticking plaster to the appropriate parts of the body for each measurement: the lobe of the ear can often be used for measurement of pulse rate with a small photoelectric transducer, as well as surface temperature with a thermoelectric transducer. Other types of transducer are used for blood pressure, respiration rate, and so on, and all the signals are

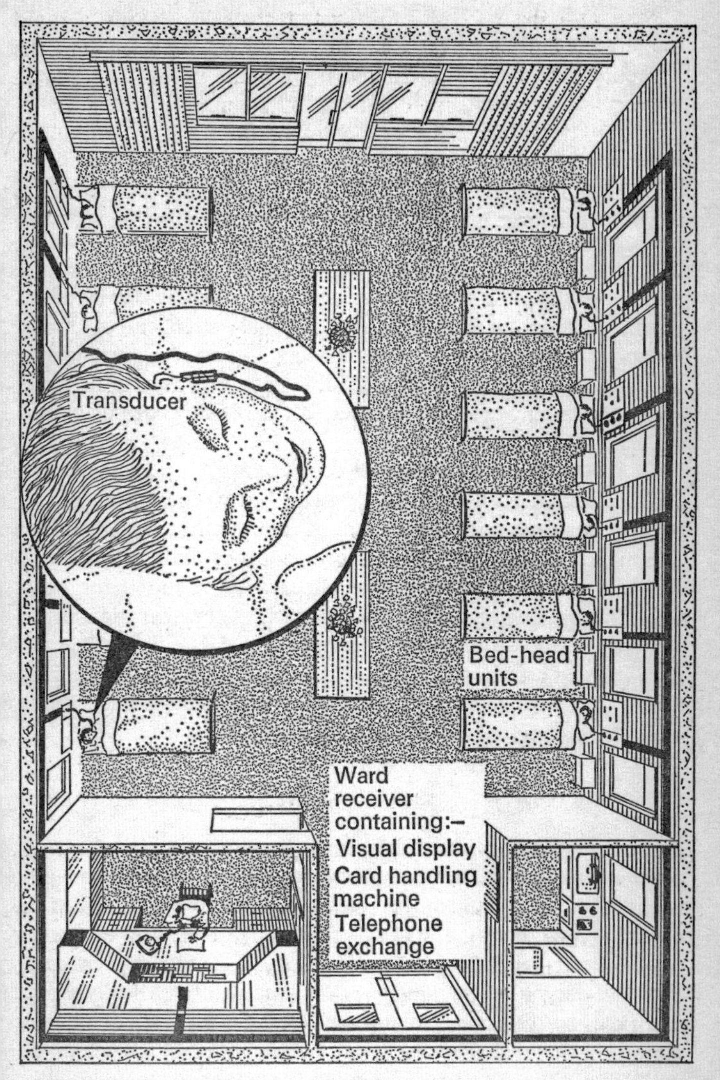


*Figure 53.* The electronic nurse allows one human nurse to supervise many patients.

transmitted by flexible wires to a small unit at the head of the patient's bed, amplified, and routed to a receiver for the ward which is mounted in the central control panel. In a typical installation each receiver would deal with about twenty patients. Measurements from the transducers are taken automatically at intervals of less than a minute and the data recorded automatically on punched cards. If any measurement should rise or fall outside the limits set for each patient, an alarm is sounded at the central console and the patient's number flashes on the panel. If a nurse wishes to know the condition of any patient, she dials the bed number of the patient and the information is boldly displayed on the panel. A doctor examining an individual patient can obtain an immediate check on the functions being measured by means of a mobile unit which can be plugged into each bed-head unit. If the appropriate punched card is inserted the readings are displayed on the mobile unit.

Of course, the electronic nurse does not replace a human nurse for the care of each individual patient but it does allow her to employ her time and skill to the maximum effect, and with the present acute shortage of nurses in our hospitals it would be of great value in the very close supervision required for post-operative patients. Its initial cost is considered rather high but to some extent this is a matter of supply and demand, and I think it will become standard equipment in the hospital wards of the future, just as the television monitor and automatic anaesthesia control will become standard in the operating theatre.

## REVOLUTIONARY METHODS IN MEDICINE

It is but a step from the measurement and monitoring of human organs to the automatic control of those organs. Some of the most remarkable developments in the application of electronics to medicine have been made in this field. One of the first organs to receive electronic assistance was the heart. The cardiac pacemaker is a self-contained portable device which automatically emits electrical pulses to stimulate a faltering heart or to correct abnormal rhythms. The device can be implanted in the chest wall with wire connexions to a small dry battery. A small cardiac monitor can be used in association with the pacemaker; it keeps track of the heart rate and activates the pacemaker when necessary, sounding a high-pitched alarm and broadcasting an alarm signal over a range of two and a half miles in an emergency. The patient with heart disease is thus literally given a new lease of life and is assured of help in the shortest possible time in the event of a crisis. Recently (1966) body heat has been used successfully as the energy source for the pacemaker, so that batteries need not be replaced periodically.

An extension of this principle of automatic control is now being studied by a group in Los Angeles led by Dr J. Lyman. They hope to achieve automatic management of diabetic subjects by continuous sensing of the blood-sugar level so that insulin can be released into the blood stream according to the immediate physiological needs of the subject and not according to the clock.

Experiments have now reached an advanced stage – notably in Massachusetts General Hospital and St Thomas's Hospital, London – to design artificial limbs which are controlled by the natural electrical signals from the nerves. Such signals are sent by the brain along the nerves to trigger off muscle contraction when we wish to move a limb. By amplifying and manipulating these small signals with built-in electronic devices they can be used to control servomechanisms which actuate the artificial limb. The artificial limb can therefore be used with the voluntary control of the user.

We can reasonably expect that an extension of the techniques which have given us artificial hearing, speech, hearts, lungs, kidneys and limbs will before long be used to make good almost any serious loss of natural function of the human body so that man will no longer be entirely at the mercy of disease or natural misfortune.

# 11

# Culture for the Common Man

What have you gentlemen done with my child? The radio was conceived as a potent instrumentality for culture, fine music, the uplifting of America's mass intelligence. You have debased this child, you have sent him out in the streets in rags of ragtime, tatters of jive and boogie-woogie, to collect money from all and sundry.

Lee de Forest:
*to executives of the American radio industry*

Our television will not show canned programmes about gangsters or good cowboys and bad Indians... or middle-class love in Chicago or Liverpool.... Its aim will be education in the broadest and purest sense. It must assist in the Socialist transformation of Ghana.

*From a statement by Dr Nkrumah*
*in a handbook on Ghana television*

ONE aspect of the electronic revolution with which we are all familiar is the widespread use of electronic devices for entertainment. I use the word 'entertainment' here in the manner in which it is employed in the electronics industry: to describe one of the three main types of application of electronic equipment – military, industrial and entertainment. No doubt several of the rapidly growing branches, such as the electromedical, will soon be added to the list of major applications but up to now the three listed have shared about equally in the prodigious post-war growth of the electronics industry, and each is a major industry in itself. 'Entertainment' electronics thus covers a multitude of sins, which include domestic radio and television receivers by the million, portable transistor sets whose numbers have reached epidemic proportions, expensive high-fidelity sound recorders and reproducers and cheap low-fidelity record players. We have to group with these the billions of discs and the smaller number of magnetic tapes, video tapes and even the sound-films destined for television screening, which represent the 'cans' for the canned programmes.

With the aid of these mass-produced articles and all the modern marvels of electronic communications which we have already surveyed, armies of technicians, craftsmen, artists, performers, reporters, writers and readers, producers and reproducers, contrive to pour out a flood of mass-produced entertainment, news, instruction, propaganda – all the varied sights and sounds of the worlds of fact and fiction – for the eyes and ears of the world's millions. The vast majority are now subjected, willingly or unwillingly, to the pervasive influence of such broadcasts all their lives. What effect will this have on them? This seems to me much too big and complex a subject to paint in the black and white of the quotations at the head of this chapter, although I think both are relevant. Whether the eyes of the multitude are opened or whether they are lulled to sleep; whether their ears are battered by all the cacophony of a commercialized culture or refined by the music of the masters; whether their knowledge is increased or their sales resistance reduced; whether their youth is exploited or their old age comforted – all depends on who own and operate the mass-media channels, for it is *they* who decide what shall be transmitted through those channels.

In his Penguin book on *Communications*, Raymond Williams classifies broadcasting into four different kinds of system: the commercial, e.g. the U.S.A. and I.T.A.; the paternal, e.g. the B.B.C.; the authoritarian, e.g. the Soviet Union; and an imaginary group, called democratic, which combines complete public ownership with syndicalist workers' control. A brief description of the main characteristics of the first three of these systems demonstrates how those who pay the piper call the tune.

The American broadcasting networks form the outstanding example of privately owned and aggressively profit-seeking systems. Before any broadcasting station is allowed to function in America a licence must be obtained from the Federal Communications Commission, established in 1934, which allocates wavelengths and fixes the times during which stations may be on the air. Not even the most rugged champion of private enterprise can escape the necessity to keep strictly to the F.C.C. rules and standards, but assuming that these are observed and that very considerable funds are available, anyone can build and operate a radio or television station in the U.S.A. The owner may broadcast whatever material he chooses, but in the normal course of events would probably affiliate his station to one of the big networks and so share the majority of his programme material with many other stations. The largest of the American networks is the Mutual Broadcasting System (MBS) but three others, the American Broadcasting Company (ABC), the Columbia Broadcasting System (CBS), and the National Broadcasting Company (NBC), operate on a continental scale, and in addition there are smaller national and regional networks. Most of the large cities have their own networks. With almost every American owning a radio receiver, and one in three owning a television receiver, it is very difficult to get away from the networks even in the sparsely populated parts of the country.

Only about 25 of more than 500 broadcasting stations in America transmit educational programmes and the funds for these come from private grants supplied by foundations and trusts. The great majority get their revenue from the sale of advertising time and they have found that the most effective wrapping for advertising is 'entertainment' and 'news'. Some advertisers are local sponsors trading directly with the station concerned, but most place their business through the big New York advertising agencies who deal with the networks on a national scale. An American citizen does at least pay a nominal sum for a newspaper but he pays nothing at all to the networks for the privilege of viewing or listening, and so has no financial control whatever over what they transmit. The advertisers and sponsors on the other hand are able to control the programmes both in form and content, and, judging by the results, they appear to have an even greater contempt for the critical faculties and educational attainments of their audiences than the tycoons of the press have. Perhaps the most disturbing feature of all is the arbitrary power wielded by the advertising agencies; since they are not directly engaged in broadcasting they are not subject to F.C.C. regulations or any other form of public control, and fear only their competitors. We need look no further to account for the tremendous contrast, which so agitated de Forest, between the fine technical achievements in American electronics and the great cultural and artistic possibilities of the media on the one hand, and on the other the stream of rubbish which turns the American networks into a sort of intellectual sewage system.

The British version of commercial television, the Independent Television Authority, came into existence as a result of the

Television Bill of 1954. Lord Hailsham described the Bill as 'evil, mischievous and ill-considered' and Lord Reith called it 'a maggot sunk into the body politic of England', but it gained some popular support on the grounds that the B.B.C. monopoly was not in the public interest. The main difference from the American pattern was that advertisers were to be prevented from exercising any direct control over the programmes and advertisements were to be restricted to 'natural breaks' in the programmes and occupy not more than ten per cent of the viewing time. Advertisements dealing with wholly political or religious subjects, or relating to industrial disputes, were banned, as were 'commercials' during a religious or royal ceremony (a major scandal had been caused during an American television broadcast of the coronation ceremony of Queen Elizabeth II by the insertion of film showing the antics of a chimpanzee). Oddly enough, makers of British commercials were allowed much more latitude in the use of substitutes for technical reasons – for example, cream cheese or mashed potatoes to simulate ice-cream – than were their counterparts in America where the Federal Trade Commission insists on the most literal accuracy in such matters.

After a somewhat disastrous start in 1955 due to lack of experience, Independent Television soon got into its stride and by 1962, when it came under review by the Pilkington Committee on Broadcasting, it had achieved such commercial success that the Committee described its profits as 'excessive' and the Government clapped a tax on them. Even after the tax the opportunities provided for the programme contractors were described by knowledgeable observers as 'a licence to print money'. The Pilkington Committee did not mention the fact that B.B.C. viewers were deserting in increasing numbers to the I.T.A. but it was severely critical of the programmes and even more of the advertisements which, it said, appealed to 'human weakness'. It regarded advertising magazines – such as the one in which the *habitués* of a mythical English hostelry continually surprised and delighted one another in fatuous conversations about the virtues of various proprietary articles – as a form of sponsoring, and on its recommendation the Government abolished them. But by then the I.T.A. could afford to employ all the talents in the world of entertainment, theatre, music and art, and confounded its critics by occasionally broadcasting items of undeniable excellence judged by the most exacting standards. However, it followed the American pattern in confining such items to the less popular times of viewing and during the peak viewing hours – for example, from 8 p.m. to 9 p.m. – tended to put out the same sort of rubbish which has been aptly described in America as the 'chewing gum of the eyes'. Indeed, more and more of this stuff is imported from America for British consumption and the capital invested in the American mass entertainment industry thus reaps a further profit in Britain.

There has been much discussion among social scientists and psychologists about the effects of the emphasis on violence and crime in commercial television on delinquency and anti-social behaviour. The consensus is that such effects tend to be exaggerated by critics of the medium. That may be, but American and I.T.A. experience has demonstrated that commercial television entertainment has been enormously successful in creating and sustaining the demand for many types of manufactured goods and luxuries by people who do not need them. In a rational world productive effort and raw materials would be directed to improving the lot of the millions of underprivileged and undernourished and it seems to me that nothing could be more antisocial than to encourage competition in squandering our resources.

The 'paternal' B.B.C. (perhaps 'Auntie B.B.C.' is nearer the mark) started in 1922 as an ordinary limited company, formed by a combination of six radio manufacturers, which was granted a licence to broadcast by the Postmaster-General. Revenue came mainly from the sale of receiving licences – through the post offices – and from royalties on receiving sets. In 1927 the company was formed into a public corporation with a monopoly granted by Royal Charter. After the B.B.C. had launched the first high-definition television service in the world (see Chapter 5) the Charter was renewed by Parliament in 1937 and the monopoly was extended to include television. This typically British method of conducting public affairs has the usual advantages and disadvantages. The Board of Governors of the B.B.C., appointed by the Crown through the Prime Minister, has certain obligations to the Government which are not explicitly stated, but it is not a branch of the Government and so in theory can exercise considerable freedom of action. In practice, an unwritten censorship is imposed by the Establishment, and in times of emergency or on political matters to which it is sensitive the Government may attempt to use its authority. Nevertheless the B.B.C. takes its responsibilities to the public very seriously and it provides one of the best and most efficient radio and television broadcasting services in the world. The licence fee is one of the lowest in Europe and an appreciable part of the Corporation's income is derived from the sale of its weekly programme paper, the *Radio Times*, whose advertising rates are among the highest for any periodical. Requests by the B.B.C. for permission to increase its licence fee in order to improve its services are treated as a political hot potato by both Tory and Labour parties.

The services provided by the B.B.C. include the basic Home Service which covers the whole country and is supported by Regional Services for Scotland, Northern Ireland, Wales, the North, Midlands and West of England. In addition three other channels are provided for sound broadcasts: the Light Programme, which, to adapt the American metaphor, could be described as 'chewing gum for the ears'; the Third Programme designed for the serious listener; and Network Three, radiated on the Third Programme frequency for the specialist minority. These programmes are also sent out from strategically placed transmitters at Very High Frequencies (V.H.F.) using Frequency Modulation (F.M. – see Chapter 4) to overcome interference on the Medium Frequency bands and ensure a standard of transmission and reception high enough to satisfy the most fanatical high-fidelity enthusiast.

The Pilkington Committee's comments on the sound broadcasting services provided by the B.B.C. were generally favourable but doubts were expressed about the policy of segregation of programme material into the Home, Light, and Third Programme/Network Three: 'From segregating programmes into classes, the next step might be to segregate listeners, to assume that there are large numbers of people who like only one sort of programme and different people who like only another, to think not of overlapping majority and minority tastes, but to distinguish sharply between "majorities" and "minorities", to think of present tastes rather than of capacities'.

The Pilkington Committee explicitly stated two principles of broadcasting. The first: that in recognition of its social significance, broadcasting in Britain is in the charge of answerable public corporations, established as trustees for the national interest in broadcasting and independent of the Government. The second: that it is the duty of each public corporation to provide a comprehensive service which will 'inform, educate, and entertain'. It did not state, understandably, that these objectives are attained only, in the case of the B.B.C., when they do not conflict with the wishes of the Establishment, and, in the case of the I.T.A., when they do not conflict with profits. It did point out that however a broadcasting service is financed it costs no less to mount, and it cannot be supposed that the service financed by advertising revenue would be the same as that financed from licence revenue. For the 'free' service cannot be offered except by an organization 'committed to use broadcasting for another purpose than the provision of the best possible service . . . and one which is, to a material extent, incompatible with it'.

The television services provided by the B.B.C. now cover 99·4 per cent of the population and those of the I.T.A. about 97 per cent. This represents a considerable technical achievement although reception is not entirely satisfactory everywhere and the Scottish Islands and Highlands are very poorly served. Extension of the television services and provision of additional channels are complicated by the technical considerations of finding sufficient frequency space described in Chapter 5. There is an extra complication caused by the question of whether to change the line definition standard of 405-lines used in Britain to the 625-lines which is standard throughout most of Europe. By going to the U.H.F. (Ultra High Frequency) Bands it will be physically possible to provide four independent national television channels using 625-lines. The B.B.C. introduced its second channel in 1964 using 625-lines and retaining the original 405-lines for its first channel. B.B.C. 2, like B.B.C. 1, achieved a very high standard technically but it soon became clear after the first few months that not enough money was available to provide a worthwhile alternative to B.B.C. 1 with its own characteristic but different type of programme. Viewers were promised a 'flexible and adventurous' channel when B.B.C. 2 was planned, but what they got was hardly distinguishable from B.B.C. 1. Although it is quite possible to have adequate funds and still produce poor programmes it is certain that the mass media cannot succeed if they are inadequately financed.

The Pilkington Committee, while generally praising the sense of responsibility underlying the programme policies of the B.B.C., conceded that there were grounds for dissatisfaction. They concluded, for example, that the B.B.C. are well aware of the liability of television to fall into triviality, but have not always succeeded in preventing this from happening. Triviality was not necessarily related to the subject matter of the programmes but rather in the way in which the subject matter was treated. Since trivial programming was a waste of the medium, it was a sin of omission; but it also had positive results and was therefore also a sin of commission. Considering television as one of the main factors influencing 'the values and moral standards of our society' it followed that the range and content of programmes should be comprehensive and give enough weight to information and education. There is no doubt that occasionally the B.B.C. produces very good programmes which come up to the very high standards we have a right to expect, but it is equally obvious that much of the time its standards are lowered to compete with independent television and the intelligent viewer finds little to choose between the channels on the score of triviality and banality.

The third type of broadcasting system, the 'authoritarian', is exemplified by Russia. Broadcasting in the Soviet Union is under the control of the Ministry of Communications of the U.S.S.R. Each individual republic has its own television and radio committees which decide on policy and programmes but an unwritten censorship is imposed in practice by the Communist Party in much the same way as the Establishment in Britain acts as the final arbiter for the B.B.C. The wired wireless method of broadcast distribution is much more highly developed in the Soviet Union than in America or Britain and most reception is by plug-in receiver. In a country the size of the Soviet Union there are good technical reasons for this method of distribution but it does restrict the choice of programmes to those provided by the central and regional authorities for all who have no access to tunable receivers. This is not really very different from the situation in countries with different political systems since only a very tiny minority in any country listen to radio broadcasts from distant countries and in the case of television transmissions it is not usually physically possible to receive them from any great distance without the technical cooperation of the countries concerned. Three national programmes, Moscow Home, the Alternative Programme, and the Third Programme are radiated from Moscow and relayed to the main regional centres. There are a large number of specialized local programmes, amounting to extensive closed-circuit networks, for particular groups of the population such as workers in local heavy industry, farmers or teachers. The rate of growth of the television services is such that by 1970 both the number of transmitters and the number of licenced television receivers will be second only to those in the U.S.A. A colour television service, already well advanced in the U.S.A. and Japan, was introduced in the Soviet Union in 1966.

Like all other mass media in the Soviet Union, radio and television broadcasting are firmly under the political control of the government, and, in the last resort, of the Communist Party. But to describe the broadcasting media simply as vehicles for propaganda is to ignore much that is admirable in them. Soviet broadcasting, unlike the kind we are familiar with in America and Western Europe, is much less concerned with entertainment than it is with culture and education. The emphasis is on Soviet culture, as rich and varied as any of the world's great cultures, but for radio the whole of European classical music is drawn on and the nearest approach to this aspect of the Moscow Home radio is the B.B.C. Third Programme. The artistic and cultural standards of Soviet television are also consistently high although probably not sufficiently experimental to please the *avant-garde* of the West. The Soviet Union now seems eager to take part in cultural interchange with other countries, including America and Britain, and their television services have already participated successfully in Eurovision broadcasts. The Russians have already used their own communication satellite to transmit television broadcasts across the length and breadth of their vast country; we may hope that this will be another step forward in the development of a world television network.

It is evident, even from our brief survey of some of the different systems of broadcasting, that the electronic media can be exploited in many undesirable ways which antagonize particular individuals, or social groups, or perhaps whole nations. At the worst this may make the presentations of these media vulgar, offensive, hypocritical or downright dishonest, sensational and distorted, misleading and mischievous, above all trivial and tedious. But surely it is as erroneous to condemn them all for this reason as to accept them all uncritically. Radio, television and recorded music cannot be contained within the bounds within which various narrow interests might like to confine them. These are essentially media with a very broad appeal and every technical advance accentuates this fact. The B.B.C. adopted as its motto: 'Nation shall speak peace unto nation', but this idea foundered on the babel of languages such as can make one tribe incomprehensible to another within shooting distance. Radio broadcasting at its best was mostly intended for home consumption, whereas much of what was radiated in the foreign language services of the B.B.C., the Voice of America, Radio Moscow, and many of the newly-formed African and Asian states, was aggressive propaganda rather than attempts to spread amity between nations. But the technical advances which produced television and replication of recorded music also created a universal medium of cultural exchange between different countries which becomes effective with world-wide distribution of recorded material and the increasing areas of the globe which can be covered by television relay, such as the Eurovision network, and by communication satellites.

Before electronics the world's great music was enjoyed only by the comparatively small and privileged section of the community who were wealthy enough, cultured enough or travelled enough to hear it properly played by the relatively few first-class orchestras and performers. After electronics the vast majority of ordinary people have such music brought into their homes and can hear it whenever they have a mind to. The transformation is so great that it is hard to grasp for those who have always enjoyed access to good music since infancy, but it caused Constant Lambert to complain about the 'appalling popularity' of music in modern times. He feared that by constant repetition even the finest music would be submerged in the steadily rising level of background noise which we now tolerate. I must confess that I would prefer a continuous musical background if that were the only alternative to the ever-increasing din which town dwellers now seem to accept with such resignation. And though I am not a lover of 'pop' music even that, I think, may be preferable to the noise of jet aircraft if one lives within five miles of a major airport, and is therefore unable to enjoy any kind of music or the bliss of occasional silence. Moreover, it seems to me that certain kinds of music – Bach, Mozart and Scarlatti for instance – well reproduced and at a comfortable listening level, are the most delightful accompaniment to leisure or quiet occupations. Even those music lovers who insist on complete suspension of all other activity when listening will concede that Mozart, for example, wrote some of his best music for the cafés.

Television overcomes many of the language difficulties especially when it is designed and produced to appeal to the widest possible audience. The best television can overcome the language problem completely. The paradoxical thing about television is that when it is put together to provide brief entertainment for the lowest common denominator viewer it often turns out to be very dull and uninteresting. But when made with integrity and sincerity to enlighten, educate or even move its audience to compassion it can result in enthralling entertainment and a work of art in its own right. At any rate it is useless to try to ignore television or to treat it as unfit for civilized people. Television is already swallowing the film industry and may well swallow all presentation of graphic arts to the ordinary men and women of the future. Formal education will come to use it to an increasing extent. In the Stone Age culture was acquired largely by word of mouth and from hand to hand. In the Renaissance it spread through travel, painting, architecture, printing. In our time it is the electronic media above all which will bring culture to the millions – the culture of the common man.

# PART THREE

# Towards Tomorrow's World

# 12

# The Science of Government

To live effectively is to live with adequate information. Norbert Wiener:
*The Human Use of Human Beings*

THE latest offspring of the electronic age is the new science called Cybernetics. This powerful new discipline, still in its infancy, has inherited a kind of ready-made mythology. It has appeared in many weird and wonderful guises: autocratic automata, rebellious robots, mutated men with marvellous muscles, and what not. Writers of science fiction have let their imagination run riot with it; it is parodied in the popular papers and desperate producers of horrid films have done their worst with it. Some trade unionists oppose it; many school teachers are suspicious of it; all kinds of politicians declare that they welcome it. As a result most people are baffled by it but I think that it is so important to our future that it is worth making the effort to understand the elementary principles involved.

The word 'cybernetics' was derived from the Greek word *kubernetes* which means 'steersman' and is the source of our word 'governor'. It was invented by Norbert Wiener, Professor of Mathematics at the Massachusetts Institute of Technology, shortly after the end of the Second World War. He discovered later that the word *cybernetique* had been used by Ampère about a century earlier to mean the science of government. Professor Wiener found that the study of the electrical engineering theory of the transmission of messages led him into a much wider field which included: the study of language; of messages as a means of controlling machinery and society; the development of computers and automata; certain aspects of the human nervous system; and a new theory of scientific method. In his book *Cybernetics*, published in 1948, he used the word to embrace the whole of this field and defined it as 'the science of communication and control in the animal and the machine'.

This innocent-looking definition proved to have the most

profound implications for society. Some of these implications were explored in Wiener's original work, but *Cybernetics*, though it caused a considerable stir among scientists, was essentially a technical book in which many of the ideas were expressed in mathematical language. To make these ideas more acceptable to the lay public, Wiener wrote *The Human Use of Human Beings*, first published in 1950. In the later book his ideas are developed and expressed in ordinary language, and Wiener states his principal thesis that 'Society can only be understood through a study of the messages and the communication facilities which belong to it, and that in the future development of these messages and communication facilities, messages between man and machines, between machines and man, and between machines and machines, are destined to play an ever-increasing part'. In the relatively short time since these words were written they have inspired a new attitude and a new experimental approach which are proving very fruitful in many branches of science and are leading to revolutionary advances in the social sciences.

A cybernetic view of the universe gives as much weight to the concept of *Information* as it does to the classical concepts of Matter and Energy. When dealing with certain kinds of systems the information content is all important, and it may be studied independently of the physical character of the system. In order to illustrate the great scope and power of the cybernetic method I shall attempt to apply it to several self-regulating systems in turn. Just what is meant by 'self-regulating' will become apparent in the course of our discussion. The examples I have chosen vary widely in character and complexity and include both real and hypothetical cases; but they have at least one thing in common: they are purposive – each seeks some specified goal.

As the word 'purposive' may have a considerable emotional content for some readers I would first like to make it clear that, in the present context, it is used simply to describe a certain type of behaviour of which self-regulating systems are capable. It distinguishes such systems from other kinds: for instance, from the type represented by the operation of a roulette wheel, which is not (or should not be) purposive and is described as a stochastic system, to indicate that any number which comes up is quite unaffected by the preceding or succeeding number. There is no need to introduce into the idea of 'purposive' any moral element, vital force, or theological concept – any more than it is necessary to conjure up a God of Chance when the roulette wheel stops spinning. Those who feel that in the case of living systems this begs the question 'Who supplies the purpose?' might ponder, for example, the very interesting idea due to Dr W. Ross Ashby that an originally random mechanism could evolve its own purpose by a process of learning, provided it contained a system which was capable of learning.

## WATT'S GOVERNOR

Nearly 200 years ago James Watt invented a device to prevent his steam engine running wild when the load was removed. It consists of a vertical shaft driven by the engine and carrying two heavy metal balls opposite each other at the ends of arms hinged to a collar on the shaft. The balls move outwards by centrifugal force as the shaft rotates more quickly and move inward when it slows down. This movement is converted into an up-and-down movement of the collar, which in turn opens or closes a steam valve and so increases or decreases speed.

This simple mechanism illustrates an important principle of control called *feedback*; a part of the output of the machine is fed back to the input. In this case the feedback is *negative* because the less the signal fed back the greater is the effective speed – or vice versa – and the net effect is to maintain the output (i.e. the speed) constant. The mathematical analysis of this control system was carried out by Clerk Maxwell in 1868 and holds good for all other

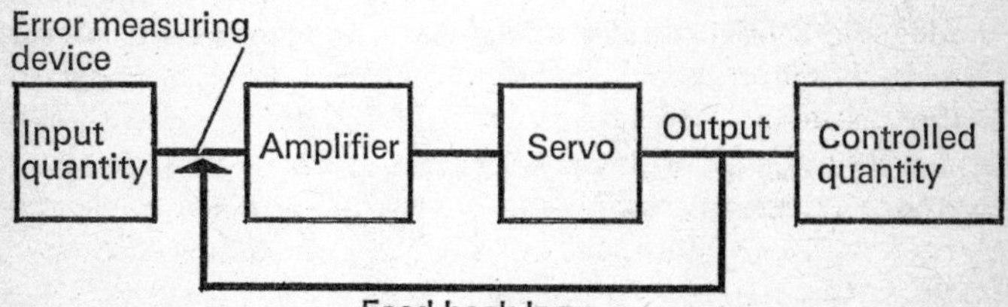


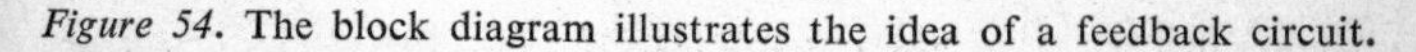

*Figure 54.* The block diagram illustrates the idea of a feedback circuit.

systems of that type. Other examples of this kind of system are: a thermostatically controlled oven or refrigerator and an automatic volume control on a radio receiver.

In cybernetic terms – which seem very elaborate when applied to such a simple system – we could say that the objective of the mechanical governor is to maintain constant speed and in seeking this objective different parts of the machine communicate with each other and take into account what the machine has already 'said'. However, the information dealt with is small, the language is a very limited one, its memory is of a very rudimentary kind, and its capacity for learning is nil.

### A MOCK TORTOISE

Some very engaging and instructive creatures have emerged from the dense jungle of wires, valves, relays, servomechanisms, photocells, Meccano bits, and so on which flourish in the research laboratories. One of these, designed to demonstrate some principles of biological control, is the electromechanical tortoise created by Dr W. Grey Walter, Head of the Burden Neurological Institute at Bristol. Dr Grey Walter, who prefers to call his pet *Machina Speculatrix*, describes its habits in his book *The Living Brain.*

It is a goal-seeking and scanning mechanism: it moves around in a series of swooping curves so that in an hour it will investigate several hundred square feet of ground. It is never still except when 'feeding' – i.e. while its batteries are being charged – and it gets round some obstacles but is stopped by stairs and fur rugs. It is strongly attracted by light of moderate intensity because it contains photocells and amplifiers connected to motors, so that when an adequate light signal is received it stops exploring and moves towards the light. Normally its photo-receptor is in constant rotation, scanning the horizon for light signals, the scanning process being linked with the steering mechanism in such a way that the 'eye' is always looking in the direction of movement and the machine is ready to respond to a signal from any direction. But if the light is very bright or if it meets material obstacles or steep gradients *Machina Speculatrix* is repelled, because its circuits are adjusted so that intense light or any slight displacement of its shell convert the photo amplifier into an oscillator and so cause it to perform alternate movements of butting and withdrawal.

The tortoise exhibits negative tropism: it pushes small obstacles out of the way, goes round heavy ones, and avoids slopes. It has discernment: it distinguishes between effective and ineffective behaviour because it loses interest in any light until after an obstacle has been dealt with. It seeks favourable conditions rather than maxima. If placed equidistant between two equal lights it will visit first one and then the other – unlike the legendary ass which starved to death exactly midway between two equally attractive piles of hay.

By placing in the head of the machine a small flash-lamp bulb which turns off automatically whenever the photocell gets an adequate light signal, the property of self-recognition was added to the repertoire of the tortoise. The light from the headlamp reflected from a mirror is sufficient to operate its response to light and it therefore makes for its own reflection. As it does so, the light is cut off, which removes the stimulus, which restores the light, which replaces the stimulus . . . so that the creature dawdles about in front of the mirror, flickering and ogling itself.

The property of mutual recognition is exhibited by two members of the species. Attracted by the other's light, each extinguishes its own light and the pair remain immobilized in alternate attraction and repulsion until an external stimulus releases them. A population of *Machina Speculatrix* would resemble a very anarchistic community since, if presented with a common goal, they would just get in each other's way. However, cooperation could be achieved by an increase in the complexity of their circuits.

Dr Grey Walter points out that it would only be a matter of patience and ingenuity to endow *Machina Speculatrix* with other senses besides sight and touch, and to provide it with hands with a different tool for each finger as well as memory and control circuits to enable it to learn to use the tools. In fact it is a valid and illuminating model of brain function as long as it is based on the principles described. If its exploratory character were replaced by a fixed programme which would enable it to carry out a series of predetermined tasks, it would then be transformed into the kind of robot proposed by Wiener to supplant repetitive human labour in factories. But it would no longer be a mirror of a rudimentary brain.

There are only two circuits in the mock tortoise and they correspond to two nerve cells in a living brain. Each of these 'sense reflexes' operates from two 'receptors': a photocell which makes the organism sensitive to light and an electrical contact which simulates a touch receptor. Yet this very economical structure can produce surprisingly complex and unpredictable patterns of behaviour. What limits then are we to set on the complexity and subtlety of human behaviour when we remember that a human brain contains about ten thousand million nerve cells?

### AN ADAPTIVE TEACHING MACHINE

Visitors to one of the Co-operative Insurance Society's newer buildings in Manchester may find themselves gazing at a scene reminiscent of the musical banks in Samuel Butler's *Erewhon.* In this temple of democratic finance a young lady may be observed fingering the keyboard of an instrument which could be taken for a tall piano. But no celestial music issues from this device – the only sound is the faint clicking of relay contacts and these are accompanied by flickering lights. Closer inspection reveals that the score for this unusual performance is nothing but a changing-number display which the performer follows on a keyboard consisting mainly of digits.

The instrument is an automatic keyboard instructor for training card-punch operators. In the upper part of the console a teaching display panel presents a series of illuminated digits which the pupil is required to tap out on the keyboard. Below this is another panel on which the keyboard positions of the selected digits are indicated by bright cue lights. The pupil at first plays short runs of digits and her performance is stored in an electronic memory. The instructions are then issued by a built-in computer according to the performance; if the pupil finds some keys more difficult than others, these are called for with increasing frequency until they are mastered. As the pupil becomes more proficient longer runs are demanded and the cue lights become dimmer. Finally, they do not come on at all and the operator is working at the maximum speed of which she is capable.

This example of an adaptive teaching machine was designed and built by Gordon Pask, a young British cybernetician who has already earned an international reputation. In his stimulating book *An Approach to Cybernetics* he outlines the philosophy on which his machines are based. 'Teaching', he says, 'is control over the acquisition of a "skill". . . . Learning is active and occurs when there is motivation. Teaching entails some effort on the teacher's part. Hence a "teaching machine" interacts with a student. Magic lanterns and simulators that merely present data do not "teach".' This interaction between student and teacher requires adaptive control systems in both. 'A brain is modified by its history, but, like any other evolutionary network, *it* does not learn. The student who *does* learn is a system developed *in* the brain. When the system as a whole is stable the two sub-systems, man and machine, are indistinguishable and the student uses bits of machine like bits of his brain in solving a problem. But this does not mean that they are physically meshed together.' This intimate exchange of messages between man and machine produces a peculiar fascination and compulsion which is experienced by most people who take part in conversations with adaptive teaching machines.

How far can we go in teaching with this kind of machine? It is not intended, and is probably not suitable, for young children but there is plenty of evidence that it is very efficient in teaching certain kinds of skill to adults. According to Pask his machines can teach any skill which can be structured, that is, broken down into a series of sub-skills which can be arranged approximately in order of increasing difficulty. This probably includes most of the skills used in industry, commerce, engineering and scientific research which are taught by formal instruction or acquired by experience. It excludes, in general, anything which demands originality and creative ability. The machines which we can produce now are not capable of the kind of inspired conversation which takes place between the best teachers and the best pupils and which sometimes results in a work of art, a lasting contribution to human culture, or a new scientific discovery.

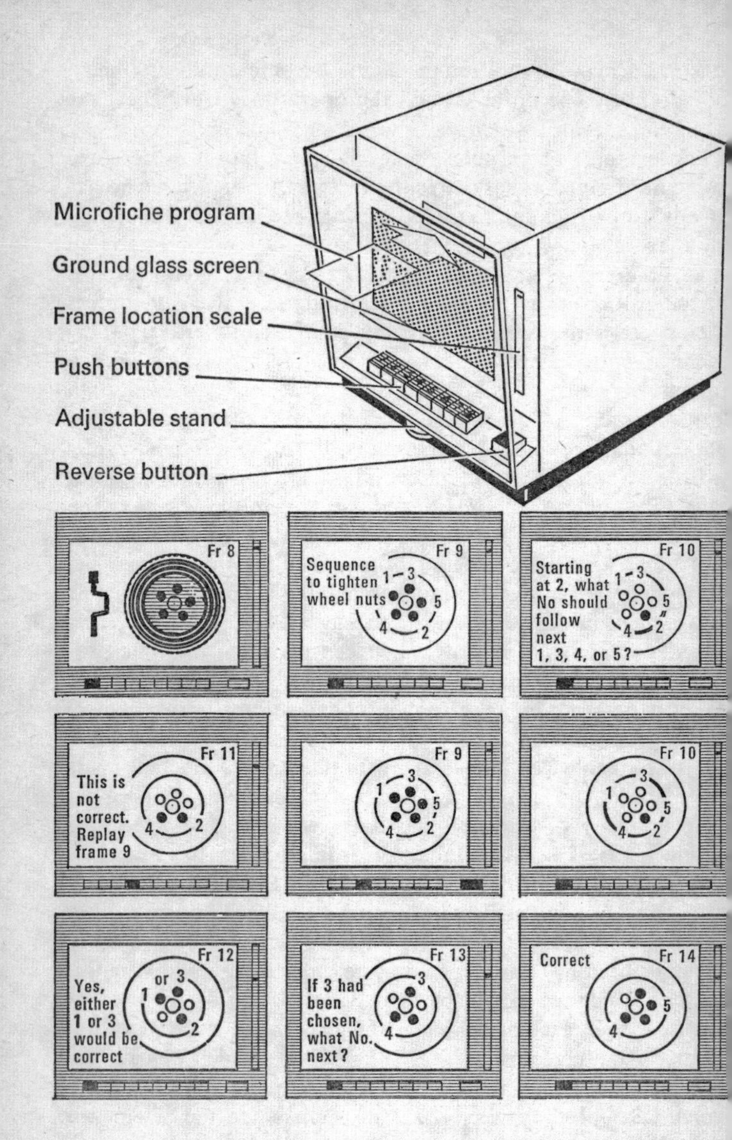


*Figure 55.* A modern teaching machine using visual display techniques. The series of frames shown illustrates a simple programmed-learning course.

## A CYBERNETIC FACTORY

The cybernetic approach proves to be very illuminating when we use it to examine a hypothetical automatic factory such as the one outlined in Chapter 7. Wiener's dictum about the increasing part which will be played by messages between man and machine and between machine and machine is strikingly demonstrated.

Matter, energy and information flow into the plant. Each is operated on in particular ways and incorporated in the products which flow out of the plant, but we shall treat the key factor here as the information. It is the information which will determine the character and efficiency of the automatic factory, what goals will be set, and how they will be reached. All operations in the factory are regulated by a master production-controller under the direction of the management. Information about orders, sales, market trends, etc., is fed into the production-control unit computer where it is analysed and combined with policy information from the management. We shall shelve, for the moment, the question of whether the management's policy is wise or unwise and note merely that the 'discussion' which takes place results in a stream of messages which go out from the central computer to subsidiary computers in the stores, the production lines, the assembly and dispatch lines.

The manufacturing processes at the various stages result from messages between the sub-computers and the power plant, the conveyors, transfer lines, machine tools, inspection equipment, assembly and packing machinery. The gist of all these messages is recorded and processed for statistical analysis, costing and accounting. Any variation from the programmed activity, such as a tool breaking or a cat getting caught in a jig, is reported immediately to central control. Our cybernetic factory naturally includes adaptive controllers and the reporting back is not just for the record but is an essential part of the process of adaptive control with which the system evolves the optimum strategy for any given circumstances. As this implies, at the least, the ability by the central computer to make decisions it is clear that some of the functions of human managers in the cybernetic factory become redundant. This does not mean that the human beings must therefore surrender their functions to the machines. As we have already noted, redundancy may be very desirable: anyone who has lost an eye or a limb will confirm this.

In Chapter 7 some of the ugly problems which accompany the introduction of automation were mentioned. They include the old problems of unemployment, underemployment and overproduction as well as the new problems of large numbers of workers with obsolete skills and more leisure than they can enjoy. If these problems are not dealt with the misery and degradation which accompanied the industrial revolution could be repeated on a larger scale with the electronic revolution. They can be solved by the application of cybernetics – provided long-held prejudices about the nature of industrial production are discarded and minority interests and arbitrary decisions are replaced by analysis based on adequate information and study of the interaction between an individual unit and society as a whole.

Consider the implications of automatic production regarded as a purposive system. What are its goals? In America or Britain the main objective is almost certain to be the private profit of the shareholders in any particular enterprise. This determines the character and performance of the system. If the goal can be achieved with half the labour force employed before the introduction of automation and there is no immediately profitable work for the redundant half they are very likely to be sacked. There are a number of alternatives: the output could be doubled with the same labour force; the same labour force could produce the same output but work only half the original number of hours without any reduction in pay; half the labour force could be trained for other jobs. In capitalist production the course adopted is mainly decided by the goal of private profit, but private profit is only one possible goal. If, for example, the abolition of unemployment were given greater priority than the pursuit of profit, one can imagine cybernetic factories employing a large number of suitably trained people for a few hours a week making articles whose production demanded the maximum utilization of human skills. According to our politicians the ostensible goal for industry is maximum production but up to now their methods of achieving this amount simply to exhortation. How many are prepared to apply cybernetic principles to the problem and then put the theory into practice? What if the solution indicated involved the relegation of private profit or the elimination of restrictive practices?

### A WORLD NETWORK

For my final example of the applications of cybernetics I would like readers to join me on a voyage of the imagination. Our vessel is a very remarkable one – a space–time machine – but I shall not bore you with a detailed description, especially as science-fiction experts will know more about it than I do. It has transported us forward in time to the twenty-first century and we disembark in New Geneva. The United Nations (which now includes mainland China) has acquired control of all national armaments and armed forces and is known as the Augmented United Nations with Teeth (AUNT). From the heliport it is a pleasant walk through beautiful grounds to AUNT's vast headquarters. Set in the grounds are various structures most of which we recognize as different kinds of radio aerial, and surmounting the tall buildings the slender masts pattern the sky with their geometrical aerial arrays. Our guide informs us that in deep vaults beneath our feet are many miles of communication cables which are linked to the international cable lines and are designed to survive an earthquake.

As we enter we are issued with our miniature personal television and radio monitors and computer interrogator which enable us to link up with AUNT's intricate communication and computing systems and so with the entire world. In the entrance hall there are a number of large television screens. One displays the vast conference hall in which several thousand delegates from all parts of the world are at work on the business of the day. Another screen displays the running totals for daily births and deaths, birth rates and death rates, and present world population. A third carries a list of the services available and the appropriate push-button codes on our interrogators. The list includes such items as:

005 AUNT INTERNAL
010 EXTRA-TERRESTRIAL
022 WORLD CLIMATE
023 WORLD MATERIAL AND ENERGY RESOURCES
024 WORLD BIONOMICS
025 WORLD POPULATION

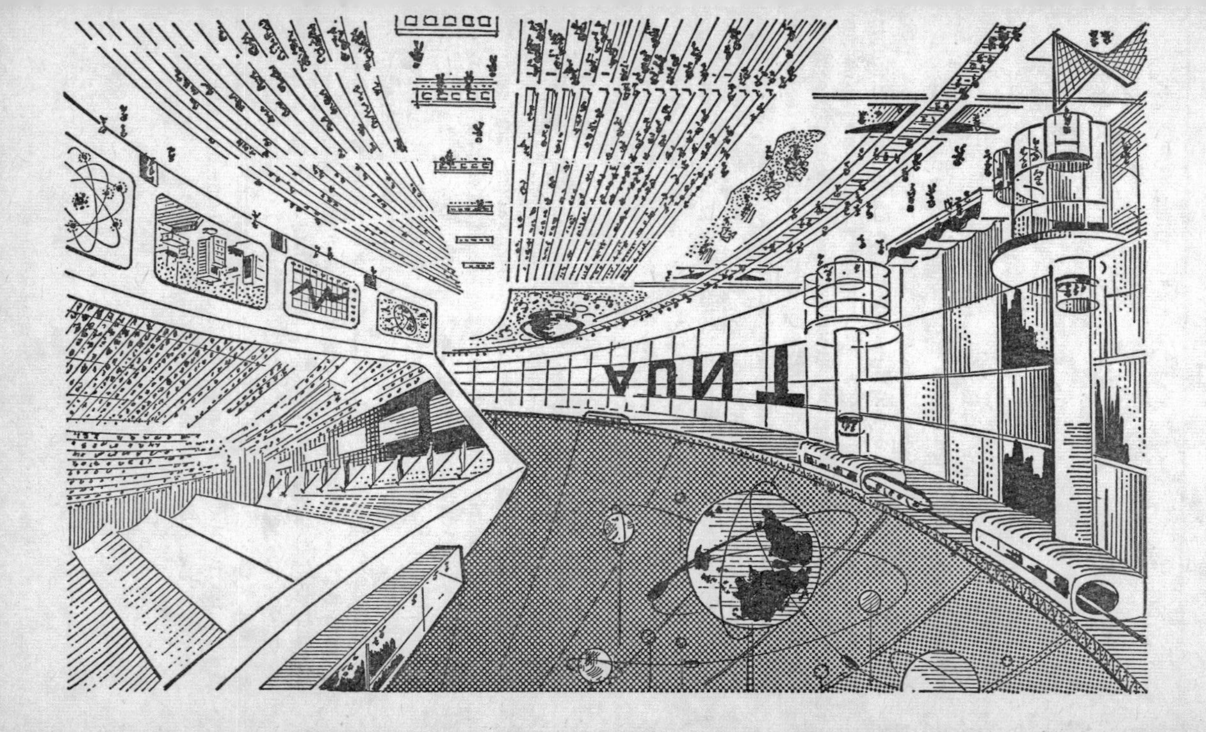

026 WORLD ECONOMY
051 EDUCATION
052 LIBRARIES AND MUSEUMS
080 CURRENT AFFAIRS

On the recommendation of our guide we press 005 and a further list appears on our own monitors: 0051 gives the history and organization of AUNT. The tiny earpieces we are wearing are soon reproducing, in the language we have selected, an outline of how AUNT works. We realize that we are at the centre of a world communication and control network on which world government is based and we have become citizens of the world.

Since the delegates to AUNT (we are informed) represent some six billion people of every race and creed, all of whom have not only the legal right but also the technical facilities to vote for or against their representatives on any issue at any time, it can justly claim to be the most democratic government the world has ever known. Through the world network the individual voting totals for each of several thousand specified locations covering the entire globe, as well as the cumulative global totals, can be displayed with a lag of less than a minute after the buttons have been pressed.

When the old U.N. was transformed into AUNT it was agreed, after prolonged discussion, that world government would come into being as the executive committee for implementing short-term and long-term plans which would coordinate and reconcile the various national and regional plans. The short-term plan, now nearing successful completion, was to ensure a minimum of food, shelter and clothing sufficient to maintain the health and well-being of everyone on earth. The long-term plan was to define and limit the total world population to a level which would allow the full mental and physical development of the greatest possible number.

Before the electronic revolution both these aims were earnestly desired by many people of good will but they had remained nothing more than pious hopes. Although the world's physical resources of matter and energy were as adequate in the twentieth century as they are in the twenty-first, the primitive social and political organizations of mankind thwarted the formation of a world network which alone could provide the information necessary for the rational exploitation of those resources. The first task of AUNT was to build up this network from the embryonic twentieth-century forms and it proved to be the work of many years, requiring all the technical achievements of the twentieth century.

Many thousands of fixed and mobile data logging stations now work tirelessly and automatically in the cities and towns, in the fields and forests, the deserts and jungles, on the mountains and deep in the earth, in the rivers, seas and oceans, in the air and in orbit beyond the air and at the bounds of the solar system . . . collecting a vast record of facts and figures to build up a comprehensive but ever-changing picture of man's natural environment. The demographic data for man's social environment – the factories, homes, schools, offices, shops, hospitals – are just as comprehensive but different techniques are used to collect the vital statistics, the medical and educational records, the expressed requirements and the actual consumption of the world's inhabitants. The world's research centres, libraries and universities are linked to the network.

The data, permanently recorded where necessary, are transmitted by radio, television, cable and facsimile to the regional centres, where continuous summaries and running totals of the flood of information which is being processed can be followed on banks of television screens and display panels. Specialized computers work on short-term prediction and offer advice on which local government action can be based.

From each regional centre the local summaries of the processed information are carried via communication satellites, radio relay and broadband cable to the world centre in New Geneva, where they are at the disposal of the people's representatives and their expert staffs. Fascinated, we watch the fast-running counts of daily world births and deaths, and the more slowly changing tally of the world's population. We use our interrogators to ask rather pointless questions, such as, 'How many centimetres of rain fell in Manchester last week?' and 'Approximately how many kilos of spaghetti will be eaten in Naples tomorrow?' just for the fun of seeing and hearing the answers almost immediately on our monitors. But the questions asked by AUNT's experts are carefully devised to test the correctness of the decisions worked out by the planning computers and to pit their own brains and judgement against the network. For although the network is virtually infallible on questions of fact there are many ways to interpret the facts, and men have been known to kill one another because of the way a word has been pronounced. On questions of opinion and imagination human brains are still paramount.

The tremendous capacity and memory of each central computer is designed so that it can be integrated with the whole network which thus becomes much more than the simple sum of its parts. It can learn from experience and from valid criticism and so acquires a sort of wisdom. Some of the computers are 'on-line' and control directly the operation of great power stations and industrial plants so that any wild behaviour of the network could be catastrophic and must be detected instantly and corrected automatically. To a large extent the equipment is designed to be self-maintaining with enough redundancy to ensure efficient operation under any conditions, but large staffs of experts are busy devising improved techniques for the network.

If this were a science fiction yarn the network would doubtless take over completely from human beings and use them for its own ends. But in fact such an outcome is very improbable since even this marvellous network cannot have more than a fraction of the purposive independent behaviour of an ordinary human being, and its objectives will be continually under review by human programmers. And the programmes suggested will stretch many human beings to the limit of their powers.

What of the danger that one small group of human beings may use the network to increase their control over the rest of mankind? This is a possibility, but why should we take a pessimistic view? Any government in which a small minority imposes its will against the interests of the majority is inherently unstable and is likely to be no more than a turbulent phase in world history. Large-scale mutual destruction is likely, but *total* destruction seems extremely unlikely. Let us suppose that we find a minority group is about to seize control in New Geneva. We have only to step into our space–time machine and pluck up the courage to move sufficiently far into the future to find that human society, whether of the twenty-second or thirty-second century, has taken its destiny firmly into its own hands.

# 13

# The Continuing Revolution

> The major conclusion that arises from a study of the place and growth of science in our society is that it has become too important to be left to scientists or politicians and that the whole people must take a hand in it if it is to be a blessing and not a curse.
>
> J. D. Bernal: *Science in History*

REVOLUTIONS have become quite commonplace in the twentieth century. Some of the South American variety, for instance, flare up, fizzle and fade out in the course of a long week-end. Even the Russian Revolution of 1917 which drastically changed the lives of millions and is still remembered vividly by many of the older generation, has lost its initial momentum and is passing into the history books. The revolution in technology and economics which gave us the mass-produced motor-car appears still to be going strong but there are clear indications that it is leading to an impasse in the more populous regions of the world and I think it will be largely supplanted by other forms of personal transport before the end of the twenty-first century.

The electronic revolution is fundamentally different in character from any of the foregoing. It is a continuing revolution. It will affect the lives of our great-grandchildren even more than it now affects our own lives. We have not yet felt its full impact although it is seventy years since the electron was discovered, but far from losing momentum this revolution is gathering it. I have tried to indicate how it will affect various aspects of our lives in the near future by extrapolating some existing trends but the time scale for these predictions could be altered by unpredictable factors – by a full-scale nuclear war for example. But whatever the detailed pattern which emerges or the actual time scale, I regard the continued development of the electronic revolution as certain. I have already mentioned in earlier chapters the physical facts on which I base this reasoning but I shall summarize them briefly here.

The electron is a completely universal fundamental particle. An electron on the surface of a star in some distant galaxy has essentially the same properties as one on the surface of our own sun, or in the atoms of our planet. It is stable and long-lived. For all practical purposes it is indestructible and is present in the universe in inexhaustible numbers. Its mass and charge are so small that it offers the most subtle way we know of probing the universe. It is also the most nimble of all stable particles; the oppositely charged stable particle present in all atoms – the proton – is nearly 2,000 times as massive. Electron devices and electronic techniques can therefore be used as effectively in any terrestrial environment as in the near vacuum of outer space with unrivalled speed of response and sensitivity. Electron devices convey information more efficiently than any other kind and lend themselves to the control and regulation of small or large amounts of power. As far as we know this state of affairs will continue as long as the solar system exists, but we can readily visualize conditions in which steam, compressed air or living things could not exist.

It seems very probable, therefore, that electronics will dominate technology even in the distant future, and I think we are justified in this final chapter in speculating a little further on how it will shape our future. Despite all the marvels of science and technology which have crowded the twentieth century, with their promise of plenty for all, the greater part of the human race is still faced with the same basic problems which consumed the energies of their primitive ancestors: to obtain adequate supplies of food, clothing and shelter. This chronic inability to ensure the fair distribution of the world's abundant resources of food, materials and energy is more a political problem than a technical one. In the previous chapter I have indicated one possible political solution which would allow our advanced technology to be fully utilized for the common good. In this chapter we may assume that some kind of political solution will be found and we shall concentrate on the technical side.

The full-scale application of electronics to our basic needs, which will appear both as one of the causes as well as one of the effects of increased cooperation between nations and social groups at different stages of development, will raise the material standards of the under-privileged majority of the world's population to those now enjoyed by the fortunate minority. Although it is likely that by the end of this century the world's population will have increased to about six billion, there is no technical reason why the resources of material and energy which can be tapped by the proper use of modern technology cannot support a population of this size. This is not to suggest that the existing rate of increase will continue unchecked. Even if the technology of the twenty-second century were capable of supplying the material needs of

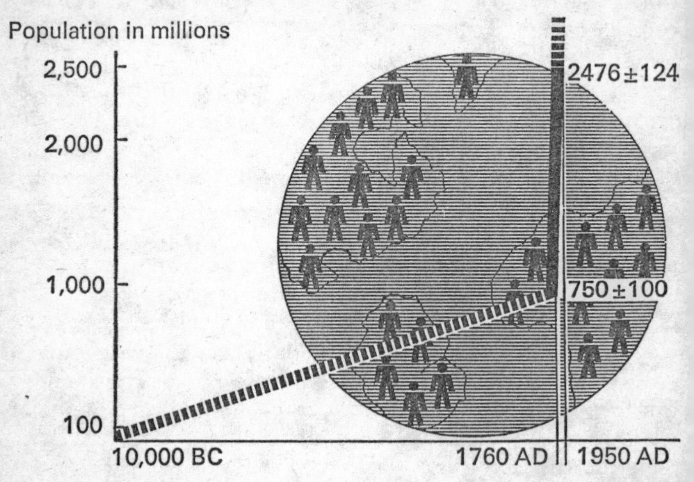


*Figure 57.* The graph shows that the increase in world population during the last two centuries amounts to about two-thirds of the present population or about three times the increase during the whole of the previous 10,000 years. (From *The Economics of World Population* by Carlo M. Cippola. Penguin 1962.)

a hundred thousand million people, the human race could not thrive under the nightmare conditions of overcrowding and lack of privacy which would then prevail – conditions which would deny any human dignity to the vast majority of mankind. But no world-wide cataclysm is necessary to reduce the rate of growth of the population. High birth rates are characteristic of technologically backward peoples and the introduction of advanced technology with consequent improvement in their living standards will rapidly lead to a reduction in birth rate.

In the last analysis the production of abundant supplies of food, clothing and shelter for the world's millions depends on the efficient use, control and distribution of solar energy and nuclear energy in its various forms. Until now we have relied mostly on more or less complex end-products of this energy: plant or animal life; fossil fuels such as coal, oil and gas; water power; and, in the last twenty years, fissile materials. Whatever the fuel, the superiority of electricity – the large-scale movement of very great numbers of electrons through conductors – as a method of distributing the power produced has been firmly established, so that the rational future development is a super-grid combining

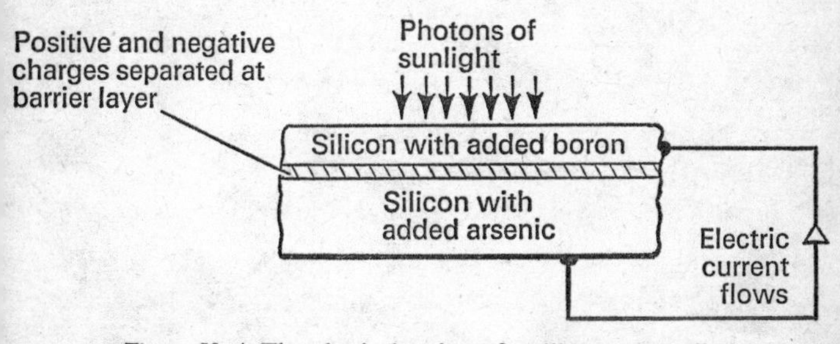


*Figure 58 A.* The physical action of a silicon solar cell.

the electricity supply grids over whole continents and fed from various types of power station. The automatic regulation and control of this great power network will be electronic.

Only a tiny proportion of the electricity at present used is obtained by direct conversion from the sun's radiation. The invention of the solar battery – a semiconductor device (see Chapter 3) which produces an electric current on exposure to sunlight – gives us one of the simplest and most efficient ways available for the direct conversion of solar power into electrical power. However large the scale on which such devices may be used in the future there will never be any shortage of raw materials since they are made up almost entirely of highly processed elementary silicon. This element forms about twenty-six per cent by weight of the earth's crust to a depth of ten miles – in fact it

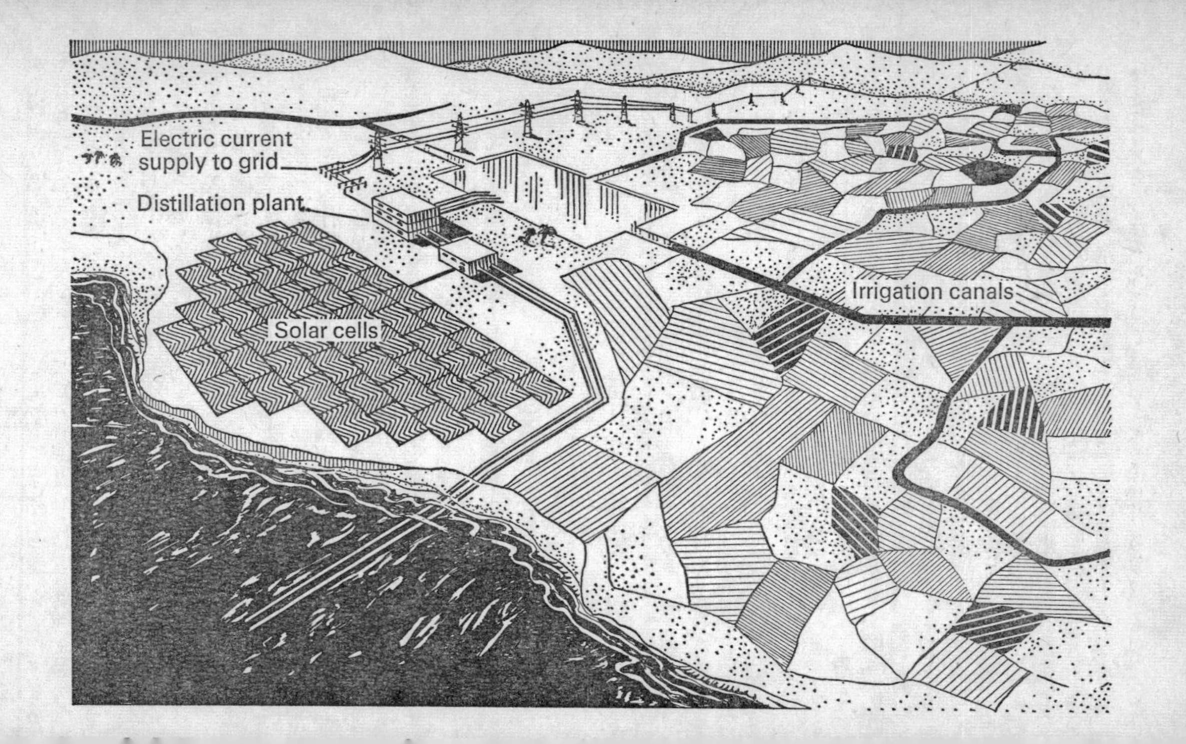
Electric current supply to grid
Distillation plant
Solar cells
Irrigation canals

is six times as abundant as iron. The energy required to extract silicon from sand or rocks and process it into forms suitable for electronic devices will be repaid a thousandfold by the ability of those devices to convert and control the main sources of power. The main application of solar batteries so far has been in providing the power for artificial satellites and space probes, but it will not be long before they are used for the direct production of electric power on earth. Whether they are installed as large banks of fixed installations in the sunnier parts of the world with their outputs fed into the super-grid, or as smaller more portable units to power individual electric motors or electric vehicles, the fact that they have no moving parts and require practically no maintenance will make them very attractive to future power engineers. They could, for example, be used to transform arid deserts into verdant food-growing areas by providing the power for desalting sea water and pumping the processed water through irrigation channels into the dry soil.

Electronic devices will also be used for continuous regulation of the humidity of such soil and for the automatic harvesting of the crops.

Thermionic emission – boiling off electrons and collecting them in vacuo from a suitable emitter – will be used for generation of electricity from conventional heat sources as an alternative supply for the grid. The principle of this method has been known for fifty years but it has only recently become of interest to power engineers because of the new techniques and improved emitting materials available.

The big automatic industrial complexes of the future will derive their electricity mainly from nuclear power which will take over from fossil fuels. Nuclear power stations will be entirely automatic with computer control. Since it is probable that the complex and difficult problems of controlled thermonuclear fusion will be solved in the next hundred years thermonuclear fusion stations will eventually take over in their turn from fission reactors and will provide practically unlimited power for millions of years. Fossil fuels, such as coal and oil, will be used far more intelligently and economically for the diverse and important materials which can be derived from them chemically rather than the crude and wasteful use of them as sources of power by combustion. If we continue to use them in the old way at the present rate they will in any case be in short supply in a century or so.

When coal and oil are treated as valuable raw materials rather than combustible fuels, their extraction from the earth will be the first stage in the long chain of physical and chemical processing which gives us the many different kinds of plastics, synthetic fibres and fabrics, drugs, dyes, paints, and so on which modern society demands. The automation of coal mining, which was described for some British mines in Chapter 7, will in turn give way to extensive gasification of coal *in situ* by entirely automatic methods which will be remotely controlled by computer. The petroleum industry, which is already becoming automated, will play a rather different role in the civilization of the future, both technically and politically. The decline of the motor-car (see below) will affect the whole economy of the world, and private ownership and control of oil, as of any of the world's mineral wealth, will prove to be incompatible with world industrial planning.

The dangerous and unhealthy business of sending men to dig underground will become obsolete not only in the case of coal but for all essential minerals. The extraction of such metals as iron, aluminium, copper and titanium from rocks and metalliferous ores will become an automatic processing industry. Driverless vehicles and robots will direct suitable forms of energy – nuclear, high-frequency, chemical, etc. – according to a computer programme, so that ores are converted to molten magma or gasified, fluidized or pulverized and brought to the surface to be conveyed to the next stage in processing. Television cameras will provide visual supervision of the work whenever required.

Robots fitted with electronic instruments, radio and television, will explore and assay the more inaccessible parts of the earth's mantle and the ocean floors so that economic planning will be based on an accurate knowledge of the world's material resources.

What of the cities and towns of the future? Most writers on this subject accept the proposition that increased urbanization is synonymous with the spread of civilization. This may have been true up to now but it seems doubtful for the future. There are many disadvantages in living in very big towns and beyond a certain size they become unmanageable. It is not so much the

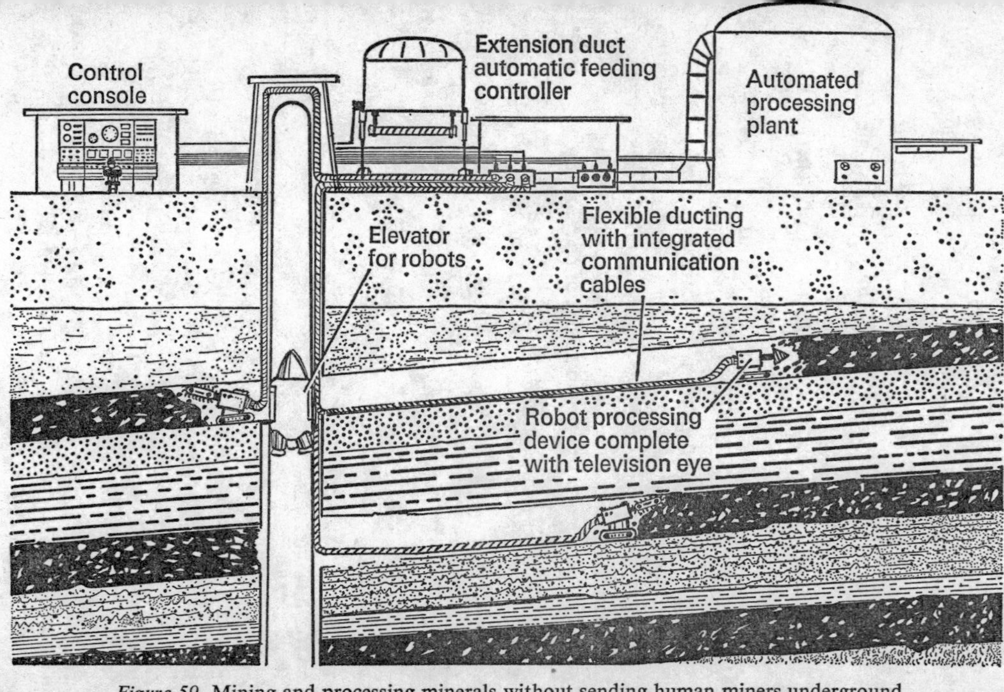


*Figure 59*. Mining and processing minerals without sending human miners underground.

advance of civilization in general which has led to the urban sprawl and spread of the twentieth century as the effects of the industrial revolution and the fact that the prevailing mode of production attracts large numbers of people into ever more crowded areas containing factories and offices. The commuter problems of the major cities discussed in Chapter 8 follow from this. But, as we have seen, through automation and universal telecommunication the electronic revolution is reversing the trend. The rapid increase in population is a complicating factor here but even this will postpone rather than prevent the eventual limitation of the size of towns.

We are not usually much concerned with problems which are not going to be solved in our own or even our children's lifetime but I think we should begin to concern ourselves with this one before it gets out of hand; the experts are not going to solve it for us. I find some of the short-term cures proposed no better than the disease, as these are usually based on accepting the need to increase the density of concentration of people for a given area of ground in cities and built-up areas. One of the short-term effects of the electronic revolution may be to facilitate the development of vertical building in the next fifty years or so, even the housing of whole communities in buildings as much as two miles high which appears to be technically feasible; but I feel sure that this cannot be more than a relatively short phase in the future development of towns.

The twentieth century may go down in history as the age of the motor-car but I do not think this particular device will continue to dominate private transport for long after the end of this century. I have already described some of the ways in which electronic control is helping to postpone the inevitable banishment of cars from cities but the internal combustion engine has inherent disadvantages which are bound to prevent cars from becoming the universal method of passenger transport of the future. They are based on the use of a fossil fuel which cannot last indefinitely, and they use this fuel extravagantly. Their exhaust fumes are becoming an increasing menace to the health of urban populations. They are noisy. In large numbers, subject to the whims of many individual users, they defeat their primary objective: to transfer people from one place to another reasonably quickly and safely. I cannot see any long-term future for them either in inter-city or long-distance travel as this will probably be better managed by high-speed electrically powered and electronically controlled vehicles on monorail or other kinds of track. In spite of the enormous investment which they now represent I think they will be replaced for local travelling by noiseless, fumeless, vehicles of moderate speed powered by developed forms of fuel cell or highly compact rechargeable batteries, automatically steered and subject to overriding master computer control. One of the blessings which the citizens of future planned towns will enjoy will be the pleasure of walking through streets and avenues designed for pedestrians, untroubled by the noise and dangers of motor traffic such as are now destroying the amenities of our cities.

What will the man of the future do with the vastly increased leisure which the electronic revolution will give him? Dr Dennis Gabor in *Inventing the Future* argues with great pungency and force that this is the greatest danger facing us because most of us are psychologically unprepared for leisure. It seems to me that the crux of the matter here is the time scale. I think man will adapt to this new environment in time. Whatever the future of man will turn out to be there is no reason to suppose that it will not be a long one in terms of an average life span. It is, after all, only a few thousand years since men were naked savages, and as Sir George Thomson has pointed out, man's best efforts to kill himself are unlikely to be more successful than those of the plague bacillus or the influenza virus. He has time, I think, to make his psychological adjustment to the man-made social environment as well as to the physical environment.

In any case, is there not a concealed fallacy in the argument that man will be lost without his traditional routine occupations? It is no more essentially a basic human need to work forty hours a week as a factory hand, or a hundred hours a week at household drudgery, than it was to hunt wild animals for food. These are merely particular stages in social development. 'Leisure' and 'work' will take on new meanings in the new age and men will begin to realize their full capacities in the heyday of the electronic revolution.

# Suggestions for Further Reading

Most of the books and reference sources listed below – or parts of them at least – should be found rewarding by the general reader with little or no specialized knowledge of the subjects concerned. They were short-listed from a very long list by applying the criteria that they should be readily available, mainly non-mathematical in approach, and likely to give pleasure as well as instruction. They are grouped under a number of broad subject headings for convenience but it should be borne in mind that many of them cover a much wider field than this arrangement might suggest.

## HISTORICAL BACKGROUND

*Moments of Discovery*, Edited by G. Schwartz and P. W. Bishop (Basic Books 1958), describes the major discoveries of physical science in the words of their discoverers. A Pelican version of this book, *Origins and Growth of Physical Science*, Vol. 2, Edited by D. L. Hurd and J. T. Kipling (Penguin 1964), concentrates on the nineteenth-century discoveries in electromagnetism, including Thomson's discovery of the electron.

*The Cavendish Laboratory:* E. Larsen (Ward 1962) includes biographies of Maxwell, Thomson, Rutherford and other famous Cambridge physicists.

## THE REVOLUTION IN PHYSICAL SCIENCE

Three books which discuss modern physical theories in simple language:

*Relativity for the Layman:* J. A. Coleman (William-Frederick Press 1954, Penguin 1959)

*The Strange Story of the Quantum:* B. Hoffman (Penguin 1963)

*An Approach to Modern Physics:* E. N. da C. Andrade (Bell 1958)

Two classics by outstanding American physicists:

*Electrons, + and –, Protons, Photons, Neutrons and Cosmic Rays:* R. A. Millikan (University of Chicago Press 1935), which includes a description of the series of beautiful experiments which Millikan devised to measure the charge on the electron.

*Magnets: The Education of a Physicist:* F. Bitter (Heinemann, Science Study Series, 1960)

## ECONOMIC, SOCIAL AND POLITICAL BACKGROUND

*The Social Function of Science:* J. D. Bernal (Routledge 1939)
*Science and Government:* C. P. Snow (Oxford 1960)
*The Science of Science:* Edited by M. Goldsmith and A. McKay (Penguin 1966)
*The Hidden Persuaders:* V. Packard (David McKay 1957, Penguin edition 1960)
An economic and technical survey of the electronics industry in Great Britain from 1896 is given in the article *The Electronics Industry:* T. Wilson, pp. 130–83 of *The Structure of British Industry*, Vol. 2, Edited by D. Burns (Cambridge 1958) and there are many references to books and articles on the early history.

## CYBERNETICS

Three books which are quoted extensively in Chapter 12:
*The Human Use of Human Beings:* N. Wiener (Houghton Mifflin Co. Boston 1950) is a memorable presentation of the principles and social significance of cybernetics by one of the most original thinkers of our time.
*The Living Brain:* W. Grey Walter (Duckworth 1953, Penguin 1961), a fascinating and entertaining book which is also a model of popular scientific writing.
*An Approach to Cybernetics:* G. Pask (Hutchinson 1961), a provocative and closely packed little book by a leading cybernetician which includes a glossary of terms and a very good list of references.

## AUTOMATION

*Automation and Technological Change*, Edited by J. T. Dunlop (Prentice Hall 1962), was designed by the American Assembly, Columbia University, and is a valuable source of information about the effects of automation in the United States.
*Automation:* Department of Scientific and Industrial Research (H.M.S.O., 1956 reprinted 1957) is a very well written and illustrated report on the technical trends and their impact on management and labour. Includes a comprehensive list of references up to 1955.

## COMPUTERS

*The A.B.C. of Electronic Brains:* L. Bagrit (B.B.C.) Based on a series of broadcast talks, this pamphlet assumes no technical knowledge whatever.

*An Introduction to Number Scales and Computers:* F. J. Budden (Longmans 1965) is an entertaining book for those who have difficulty with numbers and want to get to grips with computer techniques.

An excellent survey by two leading experts, *Electronic Computers:* S. H. Hollingdale & G. C. Tootill (Penguin 1965), also deals with applications and gives instruction in the use of computers.

### TECHNOLOGY OF ELECTRONICS

For the more technically minded and those who wish to go further into the growth and technology of electronics a good introduction would be *Electronic Equipment in Industry:* W. E. Gilmour (Iliffe 1965), which outlines modern electronic techniques, especially electronic methods of control. It also includes a very useful list of sources for technical information and extensive references to a vast technical literature.

*Basic Electricity/Electronics* (Foulsham–Sams) is a 6-volume programmed-learning course which requires no prior knowledge of the subject and which is available from Electroniques, Edinburgh Way, Harlow, Essex.

A great deal of practical information about transistors and transistor technique is contained in *The Mullard Reference Manual of Transistor Circuits:* (Mullard Ltd 1960).

A book which will appeal to young enthusiasts is *Electronics for Young Experimenters:* W. E. Pearce (Bell 1966), which gives practical instructions for making transistor radars, oscilloscopes, toy electric organs, etc.

### FUTURE DEVELOPMENTS

Speculations about the immediate and distant future:

*The Foreseeable Future:* G. P. Thomson (Cambridge 1955)
*World Without War:* J. D. Bernal (Routledge 1958)
*The Next Million Years:* C. G. Darwin (Hart-Davis 1952)
*Inventing the Future:* D. Gabor (Secker and Warburg 1963, Penguin 1964)

### PERIODICALS

Popular articles of a high standard on all aspects of electronics appear in the weekly *New Scientist* and the monthly *Science Journal.* The *Scientific American* is also well worth looking at. For those who want to be well informed about the electronics industry there is a weekly paper *Electronics Weekly* devoted entirely to it.

# Index

## MORE ABOUT PENGUINS AND PELICANS

*Penguin Book News*, an attractively illustrated magazine which appears every month, contains details of all the new books issued by Penguins as they are published. Every four months it is supplemented by *Penguins in Print*, which is a complete list of all books published by Penguins which are still available. (There are well over two thousand of these.)

A specimen copy of *Penguin Book News* can be sent to you free on request, and you can become a regular subscriber at 3s for twelve issues (with the complete lists). Just write to Dept EP, Penguin Books Ltd, Harmondsworth, Middlesex, enclosing a cheque or postal order, and your name will be added to the mailing list.

Some other books published by Penguins are described on the following pages.

Note: *Penguin Book News* and *Penguins in Print* are not available in the U.S.A. or Canada.

## ELECTRONIC COMPUTERS

*S. H. Hollingdale and G. C. Tootill*

Although little more than twenty years old, electronic computers are reshaping our technological society. This Pelican explains how computers work, how problems are presented to them, and what sort of jobs they can tackle. Analog and digital computers are compared and contrasted, and recent syntheses of the two techniques described.

To survey a difficult subject so thoroughly necessitated the collaboration of two authors, both of whom hold senior posts directly connected with computers. With the general reader in mind they have taken particular care with the specialist jargon of their subject, explaining each term as it occurs. At the same time the technique of programming is given in sufficient depth to prepare a novice to cope with a manufacturer's handbook, and the computer, in its varying embodiments, is described in enough detail to give him confidence in learning to use one.

In addition the authors have devoted two chapters to the history of computers and the fascinating story of such pioneers of calculating machines as Charles Babbage.

*A Penguin Reference Book by S. Handel*

# A DICTIONARY OF ELECTRONICS

*Revised Edition*

So rapid has been the growth of electronics that you will not find the word in any English dictionary published before 1940.

Automation, radar, television, computers, artificial satellites, guided missiles, communications, and navigation – all these, with their profound effect on everyday life, are dependent on electronics, and each application contributes its quota of new words. Hence we have a serious problem of language.

This dictionary has been prepared by consultant electrical engineer with twenty years' experience in electronics as a concise, accurate, and up-to-date reference work both for those who are professionally concerned with electronics and for those who are simply moved by a healthy curiosity about our complicated world. In the definitions provided, such words and phrases as may be unfamiliar to non-technical readers are all related, by systematic cross-reference, to 'standard dictionary' words.

Specialists in electronics will find this a useful source of short, authoritative descriptions and, when they exist, standardized definitions.